THE INDUSTRIAL ARCHAEOLOGY
OF THE PEAK DISTRICT

THE INDUSTRIAL ARCHAEOLOGY OF THE BRITISH ISLES

Series Editor: E. R. R. GREEN

Derbyshire, by Frank Nixon
The East Midlands, by David M. Smith
Galloway (South-west Scotland), by Ian Donnachie
Hertfordshire, by W. Branch Johnson
The Lake Counties, by J. D. Marshall and M. Davies-Shiel
Lancashire, by Owen Ashmore
The Peak District, by Helen Harris
Scotland, by John Butt
Southern England (second edition, revised), by Kenneth Hudson

ASSOCIATED VOLUMES

The Bristol Region, by R. A. Buchanan and Neil Cossons
Dartmoor, by Helen Harris
Gloucestershire Woollen Mills, by Jennifer Tann
Stone Blocks and Iron Rails, by Bertram Baxter
The Tamar Valley (second impression, revised), by Frank Booker
Techniques of Industrial Archaeology, by J. P. M. Pannell

OTHER INDUSTRIAL HISTORY

The British Iron and Steel Industry, by W. K. V. Gale
The Early Factory Masters, by Stanley D. Chapman
The Engineering Industry of the North of Ireland, by W. E. Coe
The History of Water Power in Ulster, by H. D. Gribbon

All these books are in uniform format

The Industrial Archaeology of
THE PEAK DISTRICT

HELEN HARRIS

DAVID & CHARLES : NEWTON ABBOT

ISBN 0 7153 5291 1

*Set in Imprint, 11pt 2pt leaded
and printed in Great Britain by
Latimer Trend & Company Limited Plymouth
for David & Charles (Publishers) Limited
South Devon House Newton Abbot Devon*

Contents

List of Illustrations

PLATES

Photographs not acknowledged above are from the author's collection

IN TEXT

PART ONE

CHAPTER ONE

A Sublime Source

TRAVELLING northwards through Derbyshire—either on the A6 or by a more westerly route—one finds, somewhere near Matlock or Ashbourne depending on the road one is on, that the scenery has made a definite change. The broad flatter lands of the plain have given way to pronounced Pennine undulations and though the road itself may be a busy one the character of the countryside seems to have become less urgently industrial, more placidly pastoral, aloof yet challenging, stimulating yet remote. The experience is similar for those coming to this upland area from counties on the west, after they have passed through Leek or Macclesfield or Glossop, or those from Chesterfield or Sheffield on the east, only for them the first signs as the land rises are not of the rounded hills of limestone with their whitish-grey rocky outcrops and walls, and gentle inviting dales, but of bolder tawny and russet outlines, hills gashed with steep-sided cloughs, dark edges—forbidding or beckoning according to the mood —and walls of blackish-brown millstone grit.

Here it is that the Midlands end and the Pennines begin. Here, geographically, is the boundary between the south of England and the north.

Today, 542 square miles of this very beautiful area comprise the Peak District National Park, the boundary of which on the map resembles a right hand pressed palm downwards, with a strip from Buxton to New Mills excluded in the gap between thumb and hand, and the closed fingers stretching towards Saddleworth, Meltham and Holmfirth in the north. Just over half the park lies in Derbyshire, the remainder consisting of parts of Cheshire, Staffordshire, the West Riding of Yorkshire and Sheffield County Borough.

Contrasts between the Peak District and the lowlands which sur-

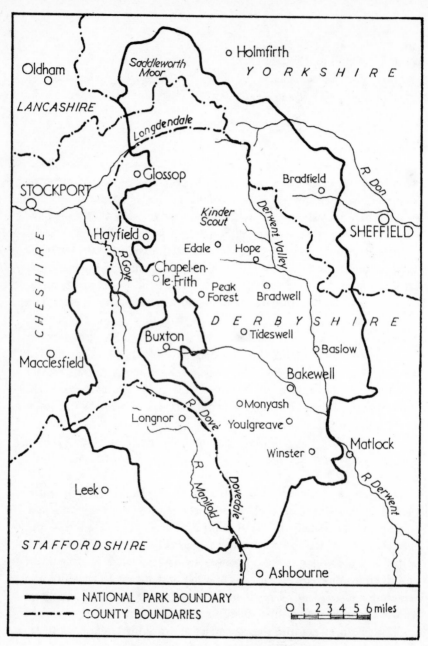

Counties of the Peak District National Park

round it are pronounced. Apart from the differences of landscape
there are marked variations of climate; and lower temperatures,
higher rainfall and a greater number of days in the year when snow
lies make the conditions for living and working in the uplands tougher
to endure. But while mist may blanket the valleys or cloud cover the
high ground, the cool air of the Peak generally has about it a clear
freshness comparatively free of the smoke pollution of the plains.
This is the significant key to another equally distinct diversity: the
contrast of the vast urban developments and advanced industry of the
lowlands and the sparser population and apparent detachment of the
upland area.

But although the wilder country may seem withdrawn from the
kind of industry which has become associated with the complex which
surrounds it, it has itself been in places the scene of intense industrial
activity, a source of wealth and of many of the raw materials sought
after in the developments of the Industrial Revolution as they became
ringed about it. The ready availability of the Peak District's particular
natural resources influenced to a considerable degree the siting and
establishment of a number of specific manufacturing industries near
its borders. As the hub of the wheel of this evolution it has through
the centuries seen comings and goings in all directions, traffic travers-
ing its hilly terrain from east to west and vice versa, and extracted
materials pouring out to various points on the circumference and
beyond.

The Peak District has been enabled to fulfil this role because of its
geographical position and physical formation and by the nature of its
geological structure. Southernmost extremity of the Pennines, the
Peak District lies almost in the centre of England, the area of the
national park measuring 39 miles from north to south and about
24 miles from east to west at its widest breadth. The northern part is
mainly high moorland based on millstone grit which attains a maximum altitude of a little over 2,000ft and extends down the flanks to
encompass on east and west the contrasting uplands of the south. A
central plateau of mountain limestone which rises to 1,000–1,500ft is

the dominating feature of the southern part and this and the gritstone are linked by an intervening area of softer shale and sandstone giving rise to gentler slopes and broad river valleys.

All the solid rocks of the Peak District belong to the Carboniferous System while in some places deposits of later periods also occur. The oldest of the rocks is the limestone, formed 330 million years ago from the accumulated remains of marine creatures which inhabited the waters of a warm, wide and mainly shallow sea that then covered the area. Evidence of this can be seen in the fossils frequently visible, and because the sea was a still one, not fed by many rivers, much of the limestone is of a high degree of purity. It varies in thickness, in places reaching a depth of around 2,000ft, and there are differing grades of texture and colour. From time to time during the limestone's formation volcanic action occurred producing outpourings of molten lava which solidified in thick beds of blackish rock known as basalt or toadstone, while at a later stage dolerite, another igneous substance, became intruded. In some places the formation of the limestone has been accompanied by the deposit of hard silicious chert, and, in a much later geological period, pockets of silica sand settled into a series of the limestone's cavities.

The limestone area has also been enriched by the depositing in post-Carboniferous times of metallic products, chiefly of lead but also including copper. Subsequent to the formation of the limestone, raising of the rock by natural forces took place, so that fractures occurred, and into these rose mineral vapours resulting from volcanic activity which cooled and crystallised in the fissures as veins of ore. The lines of these veins run from east to west and the chief minerals occur mainly in the form of lead sulphide (galena), lead carbonate (cerussite), zinc carbonate (calamine) and zinc sulphide (blende), and in association with them calcite, barytes and fluorspar.

The softer rocks, known as the Edale shales, which surround the exposed area of limestone are the result of the destruction of mountains in far northern regions and the flow of rivers which brought the finest particles of the breakdown as far south as the Peak District to

Page 17 (right) *In Lathkill Dale crystal-clear water flows from the mile-long Mandale Sough which drained lead workings of Mandale Rake;* (below) *remains of an underground flue at Magpie Mine which connected a building used for a horizontal engine (left foreground) with the square chimney. The chimney may have served an early steam-driven winding engine*

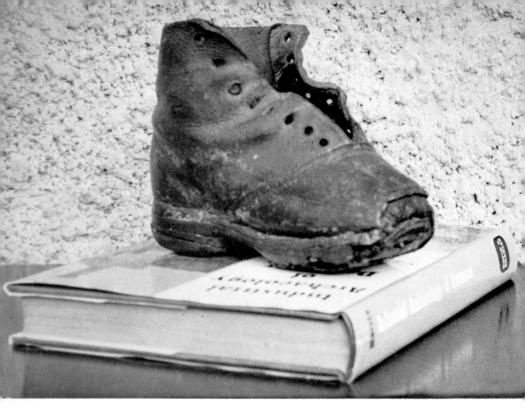

Page 18 (above) *A well-worn child's boot found in the Portaway Mine, Winster, in 1967, resting for size comparison on a book in this series;* (below) *a group of lead miners at Rake Head Mine on Moss Rake, probably about 1867. Several are wearing the basin-shaped 'Bradder beaver' hats made locally at Bradwell*

settle in the form of mud. Sinking, and the pressure of further super-imposed depositions at a later stage, caused the mud to become compacted and the shale to be formed.

As the deltaic process continued so the formation of the millstone grit also proceeded. Coarser sediments became deposited to overlie the Edale shales, and grits and gravels accumulated to form eventually a succession of sandstones, gritstones and further shales, silicious in nature and varying to a high degree of hardness. In places seams of coal also became incorporated, formed from the decay of former vegetation under conditions of great pressure.

At one time the entire area of limestone was covered by the shale and millstone grit which extended right across the Pennines from east to west in the form of a great dome. Erosion through the ages has caused a portion of the upper rocks to become worn away, exposing the denuded limestone plateau and producing the characteristic escarpment 'edges' along the boundary of the remaining millstone grit.

The geological divisions of the Peak District display appropriate variations of soil type. Those on the gritstone are generally of a sandy or gritty nature. The soils in the shale areas are mainly heavy, clayey and cold, while those on the limestone, though they vary in depth, are usually lighter and more friable. Because of the variation in the nature of the soils and underlying rocks the fate of the water which precipitates in the form of rain or snow differs widely also. Rainfall ranges throughout the district from less than 35in a year in the south-east to over 60in in the high moorland areas of the north and on the whole the west side is wetter than the east. It so happens that much of the area of millstone grit coincides with that of the highest rainfall, and in these parts, where misty conditions also frequently prevail, the gritstone is largely covered with a thick blanket of peat; this has the effect of holding the water which eventually soaks through it to filter through the porous gritstone, and leads to acid conditions. The shales in the valleys, too, are often wet, tending to hold water on the surface and also inclined towards acidity. The limestone, however, though it

B

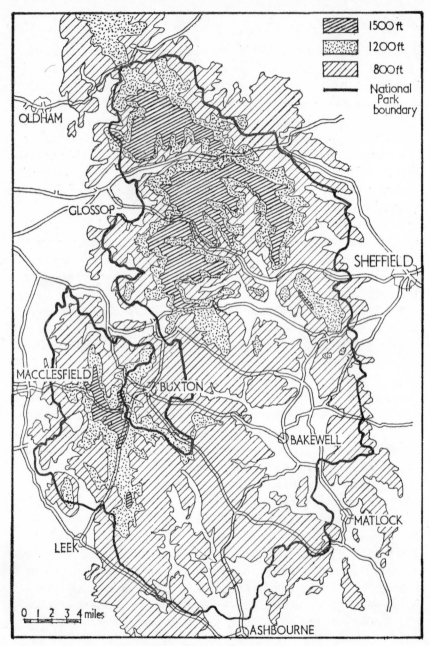

SHEFFIELD

MACCLESFIELD

BUXTON

BAKEWELL

MATLOCK

LEEK

0 1 2 3 4 miles

ASHBOURNE

1500 ft

1200 ft

800 ft

National
Park
boundary

Surface relief of the Peak District National Park

does not absorb water, is capable of being slowly dissolved by weak
acids, and since rain can be a very dilute form of carbonic acid due
to carbon dioxide absorbed from the air, slow solution has led to the
widening of joints and fissures so that rain quickly disappears through
cracks in the rocks to underground channels dissolved out of it. This
accounts for the sparsity of surface watercourses and the abundance
of dry dales in the limestone area and the copious flow of subterranean
streams which reappear at a lower level, often at unlikely places. The
overlying soil, though calcareous and inherently alkaline, in places is
subject to leaching so that the lime content may become reduced.

As they come off the high ground the waters of the moors are soft
and swift flowing. The main fall of natural drainage is in a south and
south-easterly direction, with the main river, the Derwent, joined by
the Wye and other rivers and tributary streams leading eventually to
the Trent, which also receives the waters of another south-flowing
river, the Dove and its tributary the Manifold. The Etherow, Goyt
and Dane, flowing from the north and west, eventually become united
in the Mersey while other north-rising streams drain eastwards to the
Humber.

Such, then, is the physical composition of the Peak District and the
challenge it has presented to man. This he has met and grappled with
so that rocks, soil and water have all in their several ways been
exploited, worked or harnessed as elements of industry.

Man's earliest efforts were concerned with the soil. A simple form
of farming provided the only source of livelihood in prehistoric times
—agriculture mainly of a pastoral sort but with a limited growing of
corn, cultivated in those days before the plough by primitive and
laborious means. The high limestone area probably provided the first
sites of settlement but the gritstone was also inhabited in early times,
and trees, more numerous then than now, were hewn down for
making crude dwellings. An early use of stone—though hardly an
industrial one—was in the construction of monumental burial
chambers around 2,000 BC.

Lead features early in the Peak District's industrial history. It is

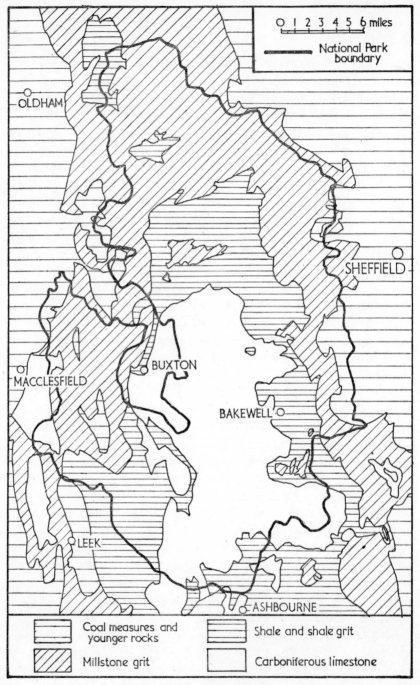

Geology of the Peak District National Park

known to have been worked by the Romans, who held the area probably for the purpose of controlling the lead supplies, and was of apparent interest at a later stage to the Danes who are reputed to have worked the Odin Mine at Castleton. In Medieval times Derbyshire, with Somerset, was the country's chief source of lead, providing for a flourishing export trade, though the Black Death which reached Derbyshire in 1349 had its effects on the industry through the shortages of labour which it caused. Methods at this time were primitive, with workings reaching a depth of probably no more than about 50ft and the ore taken by packhorses to hilltop sites known as 'boles' for smelting in fires fanned by the wind, while the miners themselves were a strongly independent body of men leading a tough existence and having their own laws, courts and privileges. As time went on methods, both of mining and smelting, advanced to reach a peak at the time of the Industrial Revolution, which also saw the highest levels of production—of copper as well as lead—before a decline set in during the second half of the nineteenth century. Today it is the associated minerals, formerly rejected by the lead miners, which are sought after and worked with profit on the sites of earlier mines.

With the progress of agriculture there came a greater need for the use of lime. For centuries previously limestone had been taken for limeburning as well as for building, but from the eighteenth century quarrying proceeded with increased intensity and many kilns were constructed. Most of the quarries lying within the national park boundary are now abandoned but, just over the borderline, extraction continues on a vast scale and is of great importance in the manufacture of chemicals and steel and in many other aspects of present-day industry as well as for roadstone, a purpose for which the associated volcanic substances have also been worked. A use for chert, one of the silicious deposits, occurred in the pottery industry, for which it has been mined and quarried in certain places since the eighteenth century, while the pocket silica sands are used in the making of refractory materials.

One of the factors favouring the establishment of Sheffield's steel and cutlery industries has been the convenient proximity of the Peak District's thick beds of millstone grit for use as an abrasive, and for centuries this rock has been utilised for the making of grindstones and millstones of which there are many relics in the form of abandoned and imperfect examples still to be seen at points along the various gritstone edges. At places just within the national park's eastern and western boundaries there remain isolated beds of the Lower Coal Measures and where these occur coal has been mined in a small way, and in certain areas clay worked for the making of firebricks. One use of the coal was for firing the limekilns, and it must have been a welcome source of fuel after the considerable reduction of the Peak District's wooded areas brought about by lead smelters and others.

The Edale shales have had less industrial significance—though they are currently worked for the making of cement—but agriculture, particularly dairying, has been of importance in the valley areas which they cover, sheep farming predominating on the higher ground.

The influence of water on the industrial aspects of the Peak District has been considerable. In lead mining its presence was a constant source of difficulty and often a hazard to life, while in agriculture the necessity frequently has been either to conserve it in areas of rapid percolation or to remove it by drainage on the retentive soils. From early times, however, advantage has been taken of the swift flow of rivers and streams for powering mill wheels worked for a variety of purposes. Originally these were all for corn, but the manufacture of paper and even gunpowder within the Peak District, and various other processes including the cutting of timber and working of metal, have relied on water power, and during the Industrial Revolution many streams were harnessed to work textile mills—cotton, wool and silk. Nowadays most of these mill wheels—where they still remain—are silent, while—just as silently—the water which formerly powered them stands in gigantic reservoirs, stored behind dams constructed in the steep-sided valleys to supply the needs of the surrounding cities and towns.

There must be few upland areas of England so enmeshed in a network of communications as the Peak District has been. The Romans were the first of its known road builders and the routes of streets they constructed are still mainly traceable. Transport was often easier on the high dry ground than on the mires of the surrounding plain, and an intricate system of packhorse routes developed on which lead, stone and agricultural products were carried. There was traffic in salt, brought into and across the district from Cheshire, and coal coming from the opposite direction. Chert went south to the Potteries and lime travelled on a multitude of routes. As industry intensified in the eighteenth century better means of transport were needed and the first turnpike roads were built. The increased importance of limestone motivated the construction of canals, and though none of these reached actually into the Peak District early railways connected them with it. In the subsequent era of railway building the topography of the district presented its own challenge to the engineers, making necessary the construction of tunnels and viaducts in the difficult terrain.

While modern developments have caused present industry to be mainly concentrated elsewhere, the Peak District, with a total population of around 40,000, has retained its rural character. Though not by any means devoid of industry it is regarded today not only as a source of certain vital raw materials but also by those who live outside it—and 17 million people dwell within 50 miles of the national park boundary—as a place for recreation and refreshment. The designation of the Peak District as a national park in 1951 was done with this in mind and industrial developments have since been carefully controlled. In the defining of the park's boundary certain areas of Derbyshire regarded by many as essentially part of the Peak District, for example the Buxton locality, have been excluded because of continued and expanded industrial concentrations, particularly quarrying. In the ensuing study, and since that county has already been separately covered as a whole (see Frank Nixon's *The Industrial Archaeology of Derbyshire* in this series) the boundary is strictly observed with one exception: being inseparable, the story of the development of limestone quarrying is to an extent followed where it overruns the border at Buxton.

And so, in a sense, the Peak District has reverted to one of its earlier uses when, after the Norman Conquest, a large part of the north-west and an area around Macclesfield were set aside as royal hunting forests so that the pursuits of the countryside could be enjoyed. Since that time there have been many changes in this countryside, with which the names of Arkwright, Brindley and Pickford have all had their particular associations. Today, though lorries loaded with lime and fluorspar, roadstone and cement thunder along the highways and milk wagons and tankers clatter on their daily journeys along the country lanes, ancient packhorse trackways and some of the former railways are quiet routes for walkers who seek freedom and fresh air. Those who explore are likely to encounter abandoned lead mines, deserted mills and disused quarries, perhaps stumble unexpectedly over the ruins of some forgotten smelting place or come across the relics of a village industry. For those who do so with open eyes such discoveries provide fragmentary revelations of life in bygone days. All are monuments to man's past endeavours and each has a part in the story of the Peak District's industrial past.

Notes to this chapter are on page 248

CHAPTER TWO

Metalliferous Mining

THE limestone area of the national park, lying almost entirely within Derbyshire except for an extremity which extends west of the River Dove into Staffordshire, has been generously and variously endowed with mineral resources. Nearly a hundred different minerals have been recorded, some in only very small amounts, others in much larger quantities. By far the most important of these has been lead and over many centuries the area was one of the country's richest sources of the metal. More localised is the occurrence of copper, yet this too has been profitably exploited, while other metallic substances, found either in association with lead or in separate deposits, have at times also had specific uses and have been recovered according to demand.

LEAD

The most general occurrence of lead and the form in which it has been primarily worked is as galena or lead sulphide, a cuboid crystalline substance varying in colour from steely grey to a bright, almost peacock blue. Sometimes fragments of it can be seen to sparkle in the light, encrusted in pieces of rock on old tips of mine waste. A less common source of lead is cerussite or lead carbonate, commonly called white lead, which has been known to the miner only in comparatively recent times, though worked in 'white rakes' in certain areas and used in the production of paint. Found in association is sphalerite or zinc sulphide, known also as black jack or blende, used in the nineteenth century as a minor source of zinc for brass making. Smithsonite or calamine—zinc carbonate—also occurs in places and

27

has been worked within the last two hundred years for the making of mortar for use in buildings. Silver has been retrieved in small amounts, but unlike the lead deposits of some other parts of the country those of Derbyshire are argentiferous only to a minute degree.

In addition to the ores of lead and zinc, gangue or secondary minerals are found associated with them consisting of fluorspar (calcium fluoride), barytes or cauk (barium sulphate) and calcite (calcium carbonate). These were regarded in former days as unwanted waste, but in recent times they have become of economic importance and further reference is made to them later.

As already described in Chapter One, occurrence of the minerals is due to the condensation of vapours produced in early times by volcanic activity in the earth's core. It is believed that this took place around 180 million years ago, the particular arrangement of the eventual settled formation being accounted for by the run of breaks and cracks in the overlying rock into which the vaporised substances cooled and solidified, and governed in places by the intruded hard toadstone or shale capping which formed barriers.

The deposits of lead are found in three main types of vein, known as rakes, pipes and flats. Rake veins, of anything from a few feet to occasionally over 60ft wide, may extend vertically to hundreds of feet in depth and run for a length of a few miles, their courses frequently easily discernible on the surface by the lines of disturbed ground, old workings and hillocks which stretch across the countryside. Smaller equivalents of rakes, from which they often branch, are known as scrins. Pipe veins also sometimes extend from rakes, and, as their name suggests, are roughly cylindrical in form, frequently connecting into a large mass of ore, often very pure, which may have filled a cavern. Flat veins lie in a more or less horizontal plane between beds of rock; they can extend irregularly through a wide area in either direction in a layer which may be as much as 20ft deep or as thin as just a few inches. The galena content of the veins varies from about 2 to 10 per cent, 5 per cent appearing to be about the usual workable average, the ore having a lead content of 86 per cent.

History

The history of lead mining in the Peak District covers the greater part of the last 2,000 years. If not exploited previously, Derbyshire lead was certainly worked by the Romans during their occupation, probably during the first and second centuries AD, and its presence must have made the area particularly desirable to them. Firm evidence of the Romans' industry in this direction exists in the form of a number of pigs of smelted lead which have been discovered bearing Latin inscriptions, including one found close to the Roman fort of Navio at Brough, near Bradwell. Some of the pigs have on them the letters LVT, an abbreviation of Lutudarum which it is thought was possibly the name given to the Derbyshire mining area. Though there is no definite evidence of any particular Derbyshire mines having been worked by the Romans some are evidently of great antiquity and it is considered, from certain typical features which have been observed, that they may be of Roman origin. In addition, extraction of ore would have undoubtedly been achieved without great difficulty by surface excavations.

With the departure of the Romans, lead mining probably saw a decline followed later by a revival as Saxons and Danes gradually settled in the area. At the time of the Domesday survey in 1086 there were seven Derbyshire lead works—probably actually smelting works serving a number of mines—which included one at Bakewell and another at Ashford. Throughout medieval times lead mining continued and increased, stimulated by the demand for piping and roofing materials caused by the current activity in church and house building both in this country and on the continent. In the fourteenth century Derbyshire lead figured as one of the country's chief exports. By the seventeenth century the number of individual mines ran into thousands and much money was being both invested and gained. The technological advances of the eighteenth century enabled a number of very rich, hitherto untapped veins to be exploited and it was at this time that the heights of production were reached. But by the year 1800 conditions had become uncertain, world demand was fluctuating, prices had fallen due to the Napoleonic Wars and around this time many mines became unprofitable and closed. The period 1830–50 saw a considerable revival but by 1860 mining was mainly uneconomic, commonly afflicted by excess of water in the workings or diminishing ore reserves, and most of the mines closed for ever. The final blow came in 1885 with the development of rich fields of lead in Australia and the formation of the Broken Hill Company so that by 1900 the decline was almost complete. An exception of one mine which continued in operation was the Mill Close Mine, Darley Dale (just outside the area of this study), a particularly rich source of lead which remained in production until the 1930s. Apart from this, lead mining in the present century has been practically negligible, though the Magpie Mine near Ashford was re-worked for a spell during the 1950s.

Laws and Customs

From early times Derbyshire lead miners had their own special customs and privileges and worked in accordance with an independent system of rights, laws and courts. These laws were first officially drawn up and committed to writing at an Inquisition held at Ashbourne in 1288 as the result of a petition to King Edward I, though they had existed previously in customary fashion 'since time out of mind', their evolution probably covering several centuries. Once written the code continued in operation for nearly 600 years—and was outside normal English law—until the mining laws were modified and made statutory by the Mineral Acts for Derbyshire Mines of 1851 and 1852.

Under the system the Derbyshire lead-mining field was divided into various separate parts or areas of jurisdiction. A large section in the north constituted the King's Field of the High Peak and included such localities as Monyash, Taddington, Winster, Bradwell and

Castleton. The southern area, the King's Field of the Low Peak, was centred upon Wirksworth (much of it lying outside the boundary of the present-day national park and therefore of the area covered by this book). The King's Field, including some of the king's manors of Domesday Book, is still vested in the Crown through being a part of the Duchy of Lancaster which controls the mining rights, while in addition there were a number of Liberties with the mining rights held by the lord of the manor or in some other way. Altogether the whole system is extremely intricate and complicated.

The centres of jurisdiction were the Barmote Courts, held for the High Peak and Low Peak respectively at Monyash and Wirksworth, and presided over by an appointed Barmaster or his deputy, with a jury of miners and others elected by him, varying in number at different times between twelve and twenty-four. At these all matters relating to the mines were dealt with, disputes settled and punishment for offenders meted out. The Barmote Courts are, in fact, still held, but less business comes before them today and proceedings are predominantly traditional.

The Barmaster was an important figure in the mining field and his duties were numerous. Any miner in the King's Field had the right to search for lead where he believed it might exist—except in gardens, orchards, churchyards or on the highway—and on finding it had to call in the Barmaster for the vein to be 'freed'. For this to be done the miner had first to provide the Barmaster with two 'freeing dishes' of ore for the king or the lord of the field, a dish being a special vessel, elongated and rectangular, or round, according to the particular place, of 14–16 pints, equivalent to approximately 58–85lb of lead ore depending on the quality. (The standard dish for the King's Field of the Low Peak, made in 1512 and presented to the miners by King Henry VIII is preserved at the Moot Hall, Wirksworth.) Having received the dishes of ore the Barmaster marked out 'meers' along the vein—of 32yd length in the King's Field of the High Peak and up to 4yd less in other areas—of which he allotted two founder meers to the miner and reserved the third as the lord's meer, all details being

entered in the Barmaster's book. The miner was then entitled to work
the first two meers along the width of the vein to an unlimited depth.
The third meer, which belonged to the owner of the mining rights,
could be bought by the miner when he had worked through the two
founder meers, in which case the Barmaster and members of the
Barmote Court had to descend the mine to view the vein and value
it, or he could work through it without selling the ore obtained.
Subsequent to the working of these first three meers, miners could
have possession of further ones, called taker meers. If, however, the
meers were allowed to remain unworked for a time the Barmaster
'nicked' the spindle of the stowes (the winch used for drawing buckets
up the shaft), and if the situation continued—unless due to excess of
water or insufficient air underground—the mine could be forfeited
and claimed by others.

Further privileges of the miners were the rights to bring water from
the nearest source for washing the ore (or to take their ore to the
water and wash it there), to cut whatever timber they needed and to
make a road—set out by the Barmaster—direct to the nearest highway. For all these the duty of 'lot' was payable to the owner of the
mineral rights, usually as a one-thirteenth proportion of the ore produced. Measuring of the ore prior to selling had to be done in the
Barmaster's presence when replicas of the official dish were used,
each thirteenth dish set aside as lot, and all amounts entered in the
book. In later days the payable fraction was reduced, but it seems
that a good deal of ore was in fact hidden and sold surreptitiously
without lot being extracted.

Another duty which was payable to the lord was called 'cope'. This
amounted to 4d or 6d a load (a load being equivalent to 9 dishes) and
was usually paid by the buyer. Both cope and lot were, by the
thirteenth century, being leased to various individuals.

The Barmaster's other duties included performing the acts of
possession or dispossession of mines and investigating the disputes
which frequently flared up amongst the miners over such matters as
vein rights. Often it was necessary for the Barmaster and members of

Different ways of climbing a mineshaft

the Barmote Court to descend the mine for a view at which miners sometimes became aggressive and strongly resistant—of necessity the miners met the tough conditions of their work with an appropriate toughness of spirit. A miner could not be arrested at the mine under common law, but only by the Barmaster under mineral law, and his offences dealt with by summary punishments. Ore could be taken in the case of non-payment of debt, and fines imposed for the first two convictions of stealing. In part of the mining area a third conviction brought a harsher punishment; the man was taken to the stowes and his right hand impaled on the wood by a knife sent through the palm, whereupon he was left either to tear himself away or to die.

Methods of Working

Early mining methods naturally were primitive, ore being worked where a vein outcropped at the surface by open workings along its length or by shallow shafts, from some of which short near-horizontal tunnels or galleries might be made to branch out. As techniques advanced, and with shallower lead-bearing material becoming worked out, shafts were deepened. Sometimes these had to pass through soft ground before penetrating the limestone and in some cases the top part was lined with stonework or 'ginged'. In some mines a single shaft was used both for the miners to descend and ascend and for drawing up the ore, but often a series of separate shorter shafts were provided for the men. A climbing shaft was usually about 2ft in diameter with bars of wood called stemples fixed at 2–3ft intervals on alternate sides down its depth to provide somewhat precarious footholds. In some cases projecting stones served instead, or the miners even had to make do with niches cut in the stone. Ladders of wood and iron were used later, but not apparently before the nineteenth century.

From the base of the shaft, drifts—or gates as they were called in Derbyshire—were cut along the vein, often forming a labyrinth of low passages. The miners worked by 'stoping' the veins, extracting

Page 35   (above) *Spoil heaps and shafts mark the site of the Mixon Copper Mine, near Onecote;*
(below) *limekiln remains in a field near Flagg*

Page 36 (left) *This once-familiar limekiln by a roadside quarry near Crowdecote, Earl Sterndale, was demolished within a few months of being photographed;* (below) *old kilns at Perseverance Works, Peak Dale, built in about 1847, closed in 1939. Open-topped, the kilns burnt a mixture of coal and coke. The lime was hand-sorted by a man and boy and loaded direct to the wagons. Rack for wagon sheets is on the left*

the ore in a series of usually upward steps. Waste rock was usually stacked into the resulting spaces or occasionally filled into natural caverns where these occurred. His only light coming from a tallow candle secured on his headgear by a lump of clay, the miner worked at the ore-bearing rock with a pick, sharp at one end and at the other end blunt, so that it could be hit with a hammer. Often wedges were driven into the vein to dislodge larger pieces. Gunpowder was not introduced into Derbyshire mines until the latter part of the seventeenth century and its use then was not general for some time, but other ingenious means were in practice for aiding the ore's extraction. One method was to light fires against the face being worked, and when well heated to make a swift application of water which resulted in the rocks cracking. A primitive kind of blasting was effected by boring a hole in the rock, partially filling it with quicklime and closing it with a bung with a hole in it; water was introduced through this hole and the violent reaction of the water with the quicklime caused the rock to split.

From the working face the ore was dragged or carried underground to the base of the shaft usually in a type of basket called a wisket, or sometimes in small wooden waggons which might have wheels and travel on rails, both also of wood. The earliest mechanical way of lifting ore up the shaft—and more latterly between different levels within the mine—was by a rope or hand-winch or stowes, with a leather bag used in medieval times as the container. In the seventeenth century, however, the use of the horse-gin had become general. This method involved a wooden drum supported on a vertical wood spindle-like post resting in a depression in a flat stone on the ground. This rotated horizontally as the horse, its harness attached to a projecting arm, encircled the mechanism and ropes or chains connected with pulley wheels on a vertical framework at the top of the shaft wound around the drum. The ore was brought to the surface in circular containers of wood or iron called corves. 'Gin' is derived from engine, the word originally used; the later steam engines were called 'fire' engines, but these were rarely employed for ore-

c

A horse-gin

winding, though sometimes a steam pumping engine also performed this function.

As the mines deepened so the problems increased. One of these concerned ventilation and to provide it special shafts often had to be sunk, with trunks of wood or pipes laid to carry the air along the tunnels. Sometimes ventilation was effected by water descending the shaft in a vertical pipe; air brought down with it discharged into the mine through an opening at the base as the water escaped another way.

But probably the greatest difficulty was the over-abundance of water. Sometimes this could be channelled away through caves and natural outlets in the rock by what was called a 'self-open', but this was not always possible and from early times methods for its removal had to be devised. One of the simplest ways was by means of leather buckets attached to ropes and raised by a windlass, but this obviously had its limitations. More effective was the 'rag and chain' pump in which an endless chain was fitted at intervals with large pieces of rag or leather, making close contact with the walls of a wooden cylinder, which carried the water to the surface in the several compartments as they were raised. Pumps of this kind were frequently powered by hand, occasionally by waterwheels and sometimes by horses.

By the seventeenth century, however, such methods were totally inadequate and in order to sink deeper mines it became imperative to lower the watertable. To do this, in many of the mines drainage levels known as soughs were driven underground from suitable valleys to intercept the mines and allow the water to discharge to a lower level. They might be quite short, or as much as a few miles in length, the usual gradient being about 10ft in a mile. Though later soughs were usually 6–7ft high and 4ft wide, the earlier ones were only 3–4ft in height and of 2ft width, so that the discomforts of the men who made them must have been intense, besides the work of breaking through the hard limestone being extremely laborious. The portals of soughs were usually stone-arched and, where their routes lay through shale, interiors were lined and the floors paved. Sometimes the branch to a sough was also a passage for miners and in this case a stone channel to carry the water, called a launder, was constructed along one side. In the larger soughs ventilation had to be provided and air shafts were sunk as well as bellows and fans being employed.

Eventually as the mines penetrated still greater depths even soughs provided insufficient unwatering. Here the inventions of the dawning new industrial age found a place. The first Newcomen steam engine in the district was installed at the Yatestoop Mine at Winster in 1715 and was followed by others in the vicinity. In 1805 a water pressure engine, erected under the advice of the younger Richard Trevithick, went into action to increase drainage of the Alport Mines via the Hillcarr Sough; this particular kind, of which others were subse-

quently installed on the same sough, was situated underground and
relied on the pressure of a falling column of water acting on a piston
for working the pump rods. Large waterwheels were also employed
around this time for operating pumps, one of 52ft diameter being
erected on the Lathkill Dale vein in 1836 and another of 35ft at the
Mandale Mine nearby a few years after—this latter was later replaced
by a steam engine. Ironically it was the insufficiency of river water
for powering them which eventually rendered water pressure engines
and waterwheels impracticable as pump-activators, and there was an
increased use of steam engines during the nineteenth century as many
of the mines were taken over by the bigger companies.

In addition to what went on in the depths of a mine, operations
above ground represented a busy scene, particularly as regards the
dressing of the ore, much of which was done by women and children.
In the early days only the purer pieces of lead were sold and the rest
discarded in hillocks, many of them to be worked over at later stages
—right up to the nineteenth century—for gleaning of their residual
lead. When the ore came up from the mine it was known as 'bouse'.
This was first sorted and the purer pieces of galena or 'bing', which
required only a minimum of dressing by pieces of unwanted rock
being chipped away, were extracted and put to store in a building
called the 'bingstead'. The remainder was dealt with on large flat
slabs called knockstones, galena and stone separated with hammers
called 'buckers' and the larger pieces reduced in size. After the introduction of the sieve in the sixteenth century the ore was then riddled
or 'jigged' in vats of water which, due to the weight variation, enabled
a degree of separation of the lead-bearing and the unwanted material,
and also graded it in size. Larger pieces from this process were added
to that in the bingstead and the residue washed in buddles. In these
inclined troughs, through which water flowed, the ore was gently
agitated, lead-heavy particles settling out at the lower level—a procedure which sometimes brought complaints of pollution from landowners downstream. On the high limestone area it was not always
possible to find convenient streams for ore-washing and in some

cases round or rectangular clay-lined pools were fashioned in the ground (not to be confused with farmers' meres), water often having to be carried to the site. Often, where there was a pumping engine, water from this was used for washing purposes.

Another method of crushing the ore was by means of a large circular stone, like a millstone, standing on edge and rotating around a circle. A shaft through its centre connected with a post in the centre of the circle, and the other end with a horse which, as it walked, caused the stone to travel along the stone- or metal-paved circumference, crushing the ore, drawn by men into its path, as it went.

A crushing circle

In the early days particularly, the majority of the mines were small ones, often worked by the men who owned them. Even in a bigger mine the owner was generally not remote and was usually considerate to his men. Of course work was extremely hard, arduous, and often dangerous, but was not without incentives. Frequently miners were also shareholders and could fare well when the market was good, and many took advantage of chances of advancement or of starting mining on their own account. Though women were widely employed on the surface for ore-dressing it does not seem to have been the custom for them to work underground, but boys did go down the shafts, and quite small boys too, judging from the evidence of a small boot found in 1967 in the Portaway Mine, Winster, much worn at the toe seemingly from the work of pulling waggons along the gates, of the size to fit a child of six or seven (plate, p 18). The boys' smaller size was of course an advantage in reaching the more inaccessible places.

Wages were not high, but miners usually enjoyed other advantages. Living often rent free, and with certain local perquisites including common grazing rights, many were also smallholders, able to provide much of their food from their own produce, and a miner commonly kept a pig and a cow and grew a patch of oats or potatoes. Bacon provided a mainstay of the diet, with oat bread and cheese usually taken to eat down in the mine accompanied, at Castleton at least, by a drink of boiled milk. Many of the early miners, it seems, wore clothes and caps made of leather, in addition to heavy leather boots. Sometimes, however, wooden clogs were worn, for an elderly resident at Winster can remember her father applying tallow to his clogs to make them waterproof when going to work at the Mill Close Mine.

Sometimes men walked from miles around to work at a mine and in addition had a long climb down and up the shafts. They needed to be strong and robust. Resourceful and skilful, conscious of their rights and eager for justice, the Peak District miners were men of independence and forthrightness. Such qualities are often marked in the characters of their descendants who live in the area today.

Present-day Remains of Lead Mining

One can hardly travel anywhere in the Peak District's limestone area without being confronted by lead-mining remains of some sort.

The most northerly occur in the Castleton–Bradwell area and here the evidence is widespread and perhaps the most striking with workings continuing away south-westwards towards Peak Forest and Tideswell. Coming south, the land around Hucklow and east to Eyam and Stoney Middleton has been much exploited while parallel to this, and south again, workings extend from Longstone eastwards to Calver. Ashford and Sheldon have mining remains of considerable interest and the signs continue west all around Taddington, Flagg and Monyash. South of Bakewell, the Youlgreave and Alport areas have been scenes of intensive working, and the evidence is repeated through Elton, Winster and Wensley along the southern boundary of the national park and beyond. In addition to these concentrations there are numerous widely distributed minor remains: very few, if any of the limestone parishes—including those in Staffordshire—having entirely escaped the attentions of bygone lead prospectors.

Commonest and most ubiquitous indications of past lead mining are the undulations of the ground known as hillocks. Now usually grass covered, these are the spoil heaps resulting from excavations or open works and shafts and of the dressing of ore. Interspersed amongst these are often depressions where shafts have been sunk, or open shafts—sometimes, as in the Eyam–Wardlow locality, crowned by beehive 'cairns' of stones—perhaps very deep, still in existence. Often the evidence on the surface bears no relation to the complex system of underground workings below; in some cases old mine workings can be entered and explored, but on no account should this be done alone by the inexperienced, or with insufficient knowledge or equipment, as such systems can be extremely hazardous. Indeed, any such area pitted with shafts has its dangers and should only be approached, if at all, with the utmost caution and extreme care.

In some cases the old lead rakes are dominant features of the landscape. This is particularly so south of Castleton, with the deep elongated scar of Dirtlow Rake, and on Bradwell and Tideswell Moors gashed by Moss Rake and Tideslow Rake respectively. Deep Rake, along Longstone Edge, is another which is pronounced, particularly at its eastern end, although current operations along it and subsequent in-filling and growths of trees make the old workings less obvious. In the case of Long Rake, west of Youlgreave, the growth of trees accentuates the line of the vein. In fact, sites of past mining are frequently planted with trees to inhibit grazing by livestock, as the presence of lead in the herbage can cause poisoning known as bellanding.

In various places, along the rakes and elsewhere, it is sometimes possible to discern the tumbled remains of small stone buildings, formerly thatched, called coes, where miners kept their tools, or of sites where surface operations were carried out. At both Hazard and Hollandtwine Mines on Dirtlow Rake (SK 136812 and 140813) remains of gin-circles and crushing circles can be seen, while a nineteenth-century crushing circle with iron-shod stone crushing wheel and circumferal iron track is preserved at the Odin Mine, Castleton (SK 135834), to the east of the A625 road as it begins ascending Mam Tor. Also at Hazard Mine there is the relic of a jigging apparatus, and another of these remains at Magpie Mine, Ashford (SK 172682). North-west of the village of Monyash, at SK 143673, is a boggy depression in the ground which is believed to have been a washing place for ore from Knotlow and Hillocks Mines which were worked up to the latter half of the nineteenth century; women employed here, it is said locally, being paid 9d a day. And south of Calver, east of road A622 at SK 239741, are the remains of a dressing floor dating from the nineteenth century.

There are many relics from the unwatering of mines including numerous soughs from which water still flows. A particularly interesting example of a sough is one constructed in the late 1770s to drain the Speedwell Mine at Castleton (SK 139827), because this waterway was designed and used as a canal for carrying out the ore and waste on the system devised by Brindley in his construction of the Bridgewater Canal to serve coal mines near Manchester. Part of the Speedwell system is open to the public and visitors can enter along the channel by boat for a distance of over a quarter of a mile.

In Lathkill Dale, at SK 197661, is the low square-arched tail of the Mandale Sough, driven between 1797 and 1820 for a distance of over a mile to drain the workings on Mandale Rake (plate, p 17). Later, in about 1839, so that the mine could be deepened, a 35ft waterwheel for pumping was installed nearby on the hillside. This was worked by water from the River Lathkill brought along a leat which commenced some distance upstream on the opposite bank and crossed the river at SK 195660, where the stone pillars of the launder can still be seen. Eventually this method too proved inadequate for dealing with the abundance of water and soon after 1847 the waterwheel was replaced by a steam engine. The partial shell of the engine house still remains and is preserved. The mine's remaining period of activity, however, was brief for it closed with a considerable loss in 1851.

On the eastern boundary of the national park, at SK 258637, in the parish of Stanton, water from the Hillcarr Sough emerges beneath its stone-arched portal to run above ground for a short distance before falling into the River Derwent. Construction of this sough, at 4½ miles the longest in Derbyshire, was begun in 1766 and completed in the main in 1787, at a cost of £32,000. Extensions were, however, added up to 1882. The sough proceeded in a mainly westerly direction, deep beneath Stanton Moor, and drained a number of mines in the Harthill and Alport areas. Its length and the fact that much of its way led through shale—a harbour for obnoxious gases—made ventilation a particular problem and to provide this shafts were made at intervals. One, of the water blast type, was known as Brown Bank Shaft, and its site is marked by a mound on the west of the A524 road at SK 231630.

Driven at a comparatively late stage, yet like all soughs representing a considerable degree of skill and endurance in its construction, was the one from the Magpie Mine. The outfall on the south bank of the River Wye upstream from Ashford-in-the-Water at SK 179696 can at times just be seen from the A6 across the river, but a close inspection can be made by approaching along a public footpath from the foot of Kirk Dale. The mine was previously unwatered by a

Newcomen-type atmospheric pumping engine installed in 1824 and by a Cornish beam engine brought here in 1868, its gaunt house-shell a prominent feature today amid the considerable mining remains at Magpie: but due to the latter's exorbitant expense in coal consumption the decision was made to discharge the water by means of a mile-long sough beneath the village of Sheldon to the river. Work started in 1873 and, in spite of the ever-present danger from the pressure of the head of water trapped behind the rocks, was successfully completed in 1881, a waterwheel at the entrance to the sough meanwhile providing power to work a compressor for the drills and for ventilation. The sough, a wide one navigable by boat, met the main shaft at a depth of 579ft, a level to which pumps could easily raise water from the further 200ft below. Work subsequently continued at the mine to a varying degree until around 1920, and latterly for a spell in the 1950s. In 1962 the sough was blocked by a fall of rock and water pressure built up; four years later the well of water erupted through a series of new openings, depositing a mass of debris around the outlet. This has now been partially cleared and the main body of water again finds its outlet via the round-arched sough tail; the volume of the partial flow—a rushing torrent even in a dry summer—is an indication of the reserves of water in the hill behind.

Calver Sough has given its name to one end of Calver village, where it drained a mine beneath the area of the present crossroads. At SK 239747 there was an engine house and chimney stack—the Cornish beam engine from here, having previously been used elsewhere, is believed to have been the one installed in 1868 at the Magpie Mine—but these structures were partially demolished in the 1920s and finally swept away around 1966 to make way for houses which now occupy the site. Water from the sough, running more or less parallel with the Baslow road, was formerly used for supplying water to the village and to feed the corn-mill pond, but this has now been completely drained to the River Derwent and the area used for building. Two other soughs, however, make their appearances nearby: at SK 242745 water from Brightside Mine can be seen as it enters an open stone water trough, and at SK 239741, close to the dressing floors already mentioned, there is the fine arched portal of the Red Rake Sough which has the inscription 'N.L. October 27 1851' carved on its keystone.

The situations of numerous mines in their respective parishes are described in the Gazetteer. There is also a considerable amount of excellent literature on the district's lead mining which deals with the subject in far greater detail than is possible here. One who has investigated the mines in depth, both in the exploratory and the documentary sense, and whose writings are standard works is Miss Nellie Kirkham. Much work has also been carried out and research recorded by members of the Peak District Mines Historical Society. The reader is recommended to the bibliography for further sources of information.

Smelting

The early process of lead smelting was carried out in primitive structures called boles. These were situated on the tops of hills well exposed to the prevailing westerly wind, often in the gritstone area at some distance from the mines. The earlier kind of bole consisted of a small shallow depression hollowed out of the ground to form a hearth in some cases no more than a foot across, surrounded by a low wall with air-inlet space for draught on the windward side. Later boles, which were in use until the sixteenth century and in some instances continued into the seventeenth, were much larger. Fuel was provided by wood, laid layer upon layer with the ore, and the melted lead flowed along channels into moulds, later to emerge as solidified pigs. Obviously the degree of lead extraction achieved by this method was not high and much of the slag by-product was further refined in later times by more efficient means.

The sites of a number of former boles are indicated by the name 'Bole Hill' which, as can be seen, repeatedly occurs on certain map sections. Incidences include ones in Holmesfield, Eyam, Hathersage and Outseats parishes, as well as such names as 'Bole Edge' in Bradfield and 'Burton Bole Edge' and 'Smelting Hill' in Abney. A 'Bolehill' 2 miles to the west of Bakewell and another at Wormhill are two of the few in the limestone area. Besides the convolutions and edges of the gritstone hills being conducive to draughts for smelting and for wafting away the toxic fumes, these particular sites, although remote from the mining areas, were not disadvantageous: it was on these slopes that timber for firing was most readily available, and the boles to which the strings of mules and packhorses, their panniers loaded with lead ore, wended their way were in any case on the routes for the ultimate marketing destinations of Chesterfield and Sheffield, Nottingham and Bawtry.

The persistence of residual lead in the soil on the site of a bole causes a variation of normal herbage and in some cases the presence of actual slag has been positively detected. There are, for example, a number of areas of bare ground marking the sites of former boles on Beeley Moor, particularly noticeable near Raven Tor (SK 280672) and at the trig point at SK 301681.

Though an advance in smelting methods had already taken place in the form of ore hearths activated by bellows and foot-powered blasts, a further development came in the sixteenth century with the adaption of water power for providing air blast to a furnace. In this system bellows, operated by a waterwheel, acted on a charcoal-fired furnace to give a greater intensity of heat. Following the building of William Humphray's smelting mill at Beauchief on the River Sheaf near Sheffield several sprang up in the Peak District, one opened in Chatsworth Park in 1574 being among the first. Others were situated at Calver and in the eastern part of Curbar parish by the Barbrook— the sites of both of these later occupied by corn mills—at Stoney Middleton and south of Hathersage at Hazleford Bridge. The Duke of Rutland's manorial smelt mill—the last in operation—was on the eastern boundary of the district between Beeley and Rowsley.

There was a further step forward in the mid-eighteenth century with the introduction of the cupola. This was a low-arched reverberatory furnace with a fire at one end fuelled by coal and a low curved roof sloping down towards the other. A low wall separated the fire from the ore and draught caused the flame to pass over the ore towards the flue at the far end which led to a chimney.

The cupola is said to have been introduced into Derbyshire from Wales by a company of Quakers in about 1747 when the first one was constructed at Kelstedge, Ashover, by the London Lead Company. Recent evidence has suggested, however, that its popularity derived more probably from developments by other concerns at Totley. In any case about a dozen cupolas are known to have been subsequently erected in the area now covered by the Peak District National Park, though only partial remains still exist.

In some cases a cupola was built on or near the site of an existing smelting mill, as at Barbrook, north-east of Baslow, and sometimes the smelting mill was retained for further treatment of the cupola slag. At the apparent site of the Barbrook slag mill (SK 268734), west of the stream close to the A621 road, there are considerable remains in the form of ruins of tumbled stone and also discernible, beneath a growth of herbage and scrubby trees, a depression in the ground which was the mill pond, with the possible route of the leat leading to it. Half a mile upstream, at SK 275739 (Curbar parish), are the remains of another building already referred to as having been originally a smelting mill and latterly one for corn. The rushy area of the mill pond here is much more clearly seen and often contains some water, and the line of the leat is easily traced to its point of intake upstream, where a wooden balk forming a weir is still in position. Also still in existence is the bridge across the stream, which gave access to the mill from the road.

Another cupola apparently preceded by a smelt mill was at Stoney Middleton (SK 224756). This was formerly known as the Lords' smelt mill and was used mainly by ore-burners and ore-buyers working independently; from 1840 the cupola was taken over as a rock mill for crushing barytes for paint making. Some parts of the buildings still remain together with traces of the leat and waterwheel.

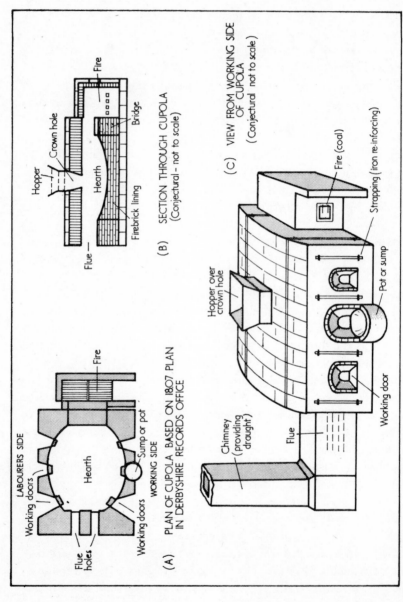

(A) PLAN OF CUPOLA BASED ON 1807 PLAN
IN DERBYSHIRE RECORDS OFFICE

LABOURERS SIDE

Working doors

Hearth

Fire

Working doors

WORKING SIDE

Sump or pot

Flue holes

(B) SECTION THROUGH CUPOLA
(Conjectural - not to scale)

Fire

Crown hole

Hopper

Hearth

Bridge

Firebrick lining

Flue

(C) VIEW FROM WORKING SIDE
OF CUPOLA
(Conjectural - not to scale)

Fire (coal)

Strapping (iron re:inforcing)

Hopper over crown hole

Chimney (providing draught)

Flue

Working door

Pot or sump

There was a second cupola at Stoney Middleton, Storrs Cupola at SK 212758, on a site now owned by Eyam Quarries Ltd. This, together with a slag mill was built in about 1777 and was in use until the middle of the nineteenth century. There was trouble here from bellanding due to disconnection of the slag mill chimney, resulting in one instance in the death of two horses. Part of the old chimney and flues still remain, together with dumps of slag.

At Bradwell there were four cupolas. Of two of them, Old Cupola (SK 176808) and Bradwell Hills Cupola (SK 178807), there is little left to be seen, and a third, Middleton's Cupola (SK 174823), is marked only by a barn. The other, which was known as Slag Works, was at SK 174808, on the east of the road junction at the southern approach to Bradwell village. Beneath the rough ground here there are still the remains of a 360ft-long stone arched flue, which runs south, parallel with the road, then doubles back again northwards for a similar distance. In the flue much of the poison was deposited by the fumes as they passed to a chimney which was demolished in about 1900. Air power came via a pipe, the end of which can be seen across the road at SK 174809, where a waterwheel was situated. A tragedy occurred at the Slag Works on 18 April 1854 when the manager, William Mitchell, attempting to correct a fault in the pump engine, was suffocated to death by poisonous fumes, as also was a workman, Joseph Hallam, who went to his aid, and two passers-by, John Darnley and Jonah Elliott, who made brave but vain attempts at rescue.

Undulations of the ground including the remains of slag dumps at SK 252822, north-east of Hathersage, mark the site of the Callow Bank Cupola, obviously well situated on the route for Sheffield, and a mill pond and leat system can also be seen. Another cupola, of which there are still remains on private land at SK 223648, was the Alport Smelting Works. This mainly served the output of the Alport Mines and was in use during the second half of the nineteenth century. There were various furnaces here of different types and much of the flue system still remains ascending the hillside and terminating in an old chimney-stack above. In addition to the lead smelted, deposits resulting from condensation within the flues was also recoverable and men entered periodically to remove it.

The former existence of a cupola at Marsh Farm, Hope (SK 163835), was dramatically brought home in 1966 when five of Mr Sidebottom's cows and some other animals died from bellanding, due to seepage of lead through the old square chimney which is incorporated in the farm buildings and the disturbance of nearby slag heaps. Belonging in the mid-nineteenth century to Robert Howe Ashton, the cupola continued in use apparently until about 1879 by which time J. H. Moore had been taken into partnership. Meanwhile, in about 1860, Ashton had constructed the Brough White Lead Works (SK 182825) by adapting a disused cotton mill and after closure of the Marsh Green Cupola the whole business was transferred there, with the premises enlarged. Smelting was carried on day and night at Brough and refining effected by a Dutch process by which white, grey and red lead were produced. Production continued into the present century under Colonel Joseph Hall Moore, and ended in about 1924. Subsequently the premises were taken over by other firms and now comprise the steel finishing works of Messrs Cooke & Stevenson. Former buildings still exist and flues partially remain.

The Gangue Minerals

Of the three gangue or secondary minerals—fluorspar, barytes and calcite—found in association with lead ore the first has, in one of its forms known as blue john, been mined for its ornamental value for over two centuries. Deposits occur in one small area west of Castleton where it has been worked in the Blue John, Treak Cliff and Old Tor Mines (SK 132832, 136832 and 135827 respectively). The name given to this particular variety of calcium fluoride, the colour of which ranges from a rich purplish blue through white to a deep yellow, may be a corruption of the French *bleu et jaune* or may have been used to distinguish the substance from zinc blende, commonly known as 'black jack'.

Page 53 (right) *Hoffman kiln at Harpur Hill, near Buxton, built about 1872 and operated continuously until closed down in 1944. The chimney was demolished in 1951;* (below) *the former Miller's Dale Limeworks which opened in 1878 and closed in 1930. In addition to the remains of the buildings and chute system the mass on the right comprises the structures of four large kilns*

Page 54   (above) *Abandoned millstones below Stanage Edge;* (below) *a 13-ton steam crane at work at the Bolehill Quarries, Hathersage, during extraction of rock for the Howden and Derwent dams. Photographed about 1907*

Though it has been claimed that the Romans found blue john at Castleton there is no evidence of it having been worked here until the eighteenth century, when it was sought for supplementary use in Derbyshire's marble industry. Blue john was used by Robert Adam for inlay work in fireplaces at Kedleston Hall in the early 1760s and also by Matthew Boulton, a pair of candelabra by whom can be seen in the Victoria and Albert Museum. By 1770 all three mines were in operation supplying material for various workshops, the first of them, established by H. Watson at Ashford, being followed by others at Buxton, Bakewell, Castleton and elsewhere, with a variety of objects, including vases and trinkets, being made. Production continued in the nineteenth century with the style becoming finer and less clumsy, but popularity declined towards the century's end. Today small quantities of blue john are still extracted and worked and sold in Castleton.

Working of the blue john mines was not subject to the prevailing laws and customs of lead mining; they were worked by local men who operated under a mineral agent acting for the landowner or tenant, with the manufacturer ordering precise requirements or even leasing a mine for a spell. Twenty tons was the maximum quantity allowed to be taken from any mine per year, with 3 tons the limit latterly. Blue john is a soft, brittle substance to work and extraction has always been by hand tools, aided at times by fires lit against the rock to crack it, great care being necessary in order to remove the mineral in unbroken pieces as large as possible. The depth of workings in the Blue John Mine reaches about 200ft. Both this and the Treak Cliff cavern are open to the public.

With the introduction around 1900 of the basic hearth method of steel manufacture, reserves of fluorspar—needed as a flux in the process—lying as long-abandoned lead-mining waste in dumps on the surface or back-filled into workings below ground, took on a new significance. Of the gangue minerals fluorspar is richest in the east of the limestone area, barytes and then calcite predominating towards the west, and on the eastern side extraction of fluorspar, stimulated

D

by two world wars and the needs of industry has steadily increased. Recovery of the mineral in the early stages was confined to re-working of the old overgrown hillocks on the surface—those in the Eyam locality being amongst the first to receive attention—but later was extended in certain cases to include opencast and underground mining.

Due to the increased demand, and in particular the requirements of the chemical industry for high-quality acid-grade fluorspar used in the manufacture of hydrofluoric acid, considerable developments have taken place in the Eyam–Stoney Middleton locality in recent years. Glebe Mine (SK 219764) was reopened in 1937 and in 1959 became a subsidiary of Laporte Industries Ltd. It is now connected northwards underground with Ladywash Mine (SK 218775), deep workings extending into the limestone beneath the overlying millstone grit of Hucklow Edge and the ore being hauled up the Ladywash shaft. Formerly, treatment of the ore for fluorspar separation was done in the limited area of Glebe Mine in Eyam village, but since 1965 operations here have ceased and all processing is now carried out at the firm's large Cavendish Mill on Middleton Moor (SK 206752). Supplies of raw material for the plant come also from the Sallet Hole Mine (SK 219741) where the company is mining underground in Deep Rake beneath Longstone Edge, and in addition from other workings of the firm, farther afield, as well as from 'tributers', individuals or small companies extracting material on the sites of old mines on their own account but without ore-dressing facilities.

In addition to the 35–40 per cent fluorspar content of the incoming ore, barytes is also present at an average of 20–25 per cent. On extraction this heavy and chemically inactive substance, which forms a white powder, is used in the manufacture of paint; as a filler in paper, textile and rubber industries; and in impure form in oil-well drilling.

The other gangue mineral, calcite, extracted at Youlgreave from workings on the old Long Rake, is used in decorative work and in special types of white paint.

COPPER

The localities in which copper has been mined lie in Staffordshire, the main source being at Ecton in the parish of Wetton, in the depths of the prominent limestone hill which centres on SK 100580.

Though known to have been worked at the beginning of the seventeenth century and probably earlier, the mines had been idle for a spell when, in 1739, a Cornish miner walking over the hill picked up and recognised a piece of copper ore and, considering the possibilities and gathering a party of Ashbourne 'adventurers', approached the Duke of Devonshire, holder of the mining rights, for a lease enabling them to prospect. First attempts were unfruitful, and the expending of much money without return caused several of the adventurers to sell out at a loss. But their successors were more fortunate and struck rich reserves which they were exploiting when the 25-year lease expired. Working of the mines was then taken over by the duke and became exceedingly profitable; in the late 1760s annual profit was estimated at £8,000–£10,000 and from 1776 to 1817 the value exceeded £677,000. The Crescent at Buxton is said to have been built with the revenue from Ecton Mines. This period was Ecton's heyday; the 15 per cent copper ore compared favourably both in quality and yield with those of other parts of the country. But in the following century, during which Devon and Cornwall were at times providing half the world's copper supply, Ecton production had fallen, and in 1871 amounted to only 1 ton a year. In the late 1880s or 90s working had ceased.

William Efford writing in 1769 gives a vivid picture, from a visit he made, of underground working at Ecton which could, in fact, probably equally convey the atmosphere of many mines of that time. The scene on entering he describes as follows: 'Indeed, such a horrid gloom, such rattling of waggons, noise of workmen boring rocks under your feet, such explosions in blasting and such a dreadful gulf to descend present a scene of terror that few people who are not versed in mining care to pass through.' Then, descending to the 'place of action'—about 160 yards—'a new scene, ten thousand times more astonishing than that above, presents itself, a place as horrible to view as imagination can conceive. On the passage down, the constant blasting of the rock ten times louder than the loudest thunder, seems to roll and shake the whole body of the mountain.' And at the bottom 'the glimmering light of candles and the nasty suffocating smell of sulphur and gunpowder'. (Gunpowder is said to have been used for the first time in a British mine at Ecton in 1670.) About sixty men worked day and night, 'naked except for coarse canvas drawers', in 6hr spells, earning 1s (5p) a shift, and in spite of their hardships Efford considered them 'as merry and jovial a set of mortals as ever inhabited such infernal abodes'.

The ore was carted out from the mine by boys, and sorted and dressed by little girls and women before being washed in the River Manifold under an 'experienced Cornishman'. More than 300 men, women and children, of ages ranging from five to sixty were employed at Ecton at that time, coming from a wide neighbourhood around. Though some ore was smelted on the site, most was taken and smelted at Whiston, with much of the resulting copper used for brass making. Up to the last stages of the mine being worked this carting of ore in waggons was undertaken by local farmers who brought back coal on the return journey.

Today there are numerous mineshafts all over the hill at Ecton. The deepest of the mines was Deep Ecton, reaching—in the mid-nineteenth century—1,380ft from the summit of the hill, where the site of its former engine house is now marked by a barn. Water for powering a waterwheel within the mine was conveyed by a wooden launder from the river on the north side across the road to Apes Tor level, drainage being by an adit to the river on the west. A 'fishpond' near the remains of East Ecton Mine (SK 104581) was a reservoir for water which was conveyed in a launder made of sandstone (said to be of stone dressed at Sheen) covered with stone slabs, and below ground around the hills to Ecton, probably originally to provide power for smelting and latterly for ore washing. Today's quiet scene at Ecton must differ greatly from that of former days, busy with the mining activity and more people living there. A somewhat conspicuous feature is the entrance to the Clayton Mine level, close by the roadside at SK 096581, but many other signs of the mines are now gone, including large waste-tips formerly bordering the roadside which were cleared away only a few years ago for road material.

In addition there were other, smaller copper mines in this district. Mixon Mine, Onecote (SK 046574), though in 1851 unworked for thirty years, was in operation in the latter part of the century with men walking here to work from miles around. Flooding is believed to have contributed to its closure. The site, on the west bank of the River Hamps, is marked today by a number of shafts, a building and spoil heaps (plate, p 35). At Upper Elkstone, on the east side of the Hamps valley, are the remains of the Royledge, New York and Hill House Mines, including the ruins of the New York Count House at SK 048591. Some old shafts at Back-of-the-Brook at Waterfall in Waterhouses parish are relics of past working for copper where, as in others, lead was also produced.

OTHER METALS

Iron, occurring in oxide form as yellow or red ochre, has been produced in various mines in small quantity and used as a colouring material. As haematite it has been found in a few areas and was used in bygone days for the making of buttons.

Manganese, known as black wad, has been found in mines particularly on the western side of the lead-mining area and there was a kiln at Wensley in which it was prepared for use as a black pigment in paint for ships and buildings.

Notes to this chapter are on page 248

CHAPTER THREE

Exploitation of the Rock Formations

LIMESTONE, the oldest of the rocks of the Peak District, has also been the one of greatest economic importance, valued from the distant past through the ages up to the present, when its extraction continues on an intensified and highly industrialised plane.

Since prehistoric times limestone has been used for building, a purpose for which its properties of durability, compactness and non-porosity have made it an eminently suitable material. The stone's attractive qualities—the texture and greyish-white colour—and the skilful way in which the usually random-shaped blocks have been handled in building have contributed greatly to the pleasing effect of the limestone countryside, instanced particularly in such villages as Tissington and Alstonfield, Chelmorton and Monyash, Litton and Ashford-in-the-Water. All types of dwellings—cottages, farmhouses and mansions—have witnessed the use of limestone in their construction and many of those in existence are some hundreds of years old. With the development of communications limestone was used in the building of railways—in structural work and for ballast—while the stone's high degree of crushable strength has made it of increasing importance in road making for which it is currently transported far afield. In some instances too limestone has been used for paving stones in towns; at Wetton during the early part of the present century stone was being cut into setts in banker sheds (no longer standing) at the quarry and sent away on the Leek & Manifold Valley Light Railway for the streets of Stoke-on-Trent.

Characteristic of the area are the stone walls which border roads and separate the fields, many of them dating from the time of agricultural enclosure, others of much earlier origin, and one wonders where all the stone was excavated. Though in early times there was doubtless much fragmented surface stone which could be utilised, quarrying has long been a necessity and local requirements were served by countless small workings conveniently sited. Frequently the stone for wall building was extracted from a ground-work beneath a thin soil layer in the corner of a field, often now grassed over and recognisable only as a depression, while small parish quarries supplied the other appropriate needs of the village. Eyam is an example of a parish where ratepayers still have the right to take stone from certain limestone quarries free of charge.

But besides its value as a solid building material, lime produced by calcining limestone, involving the reduction of calcium carbonate to calcium oxide, has a wide variety of uses, as was recognised way back in history by the Egyptians who used it around 2,000 BC for interior plaster work in the pyramids, and by the Greeks and Romans in subsequent ages in the making of cement. Evidence that lime-burning was almost certainly carried on in the Buxton locality in very early times came to light during excavations for the foundations of the Buxton Crescent, with the discovery of a Roman bath constructed of limestone and cemented with mortar made with lime.

In addition, the advantages gained from the application of lime as a fertiliser on agricultural land must have been known since time immemorial, and the practice of burning limestone in a small way for individual or local use was carried on throughout the area for several centuries, and in places up to the early years of the present one. Fitzherbert of Norbury in *The Boke of Husbandrye*, written in the early sixteenth century, describes the process of burning lime for the purposes of agriculture, and in a survey of the High Peak of 1650, fourteen kilns were mentioned as being in operation within the waste ground of the manor at Dove Holes, apparently constructed and removed by the people living there according to requirements. On many manors tenants enjoyed the right to take limestone from the waste land for their own use, a privilege which was curtailed in the seventeenth and eighteenth centuries as the wastes became enclosed.

The early burners of lime in the Peak District were all farmers and nearly every farm was equipped with one or a number of stone-built 'pudding pie' kilns. Obtaining the raw material for the process presented no problem in such an area with ample supplies of stone outcropping or lying at little below surface level. Usually the work of firing and feeding the kilns alternated with the other jobs of the farm and was done in the less busy times of the year. Lime was burnt sufficient for home requirements but where excess was produced the surplus was sold to builders for use in mortar, to tanners and candlemakers, to smelters of lead and iron (onwards from the seventeenth century) for use as a flux in the removal of impurities, or sold to farmers of other districts. Transport in the early days was by packhorse and after the eighteenth century in carts.

John Farey, in Volume 2 of his *General View of the Agriculture and Minerals of Derbyshire*, quotes the requirements for a limekiln as given in the early eighteenth century by a Mr John Milner. He states that the diameter at the top of the kiln should be about a third of its depth and that the top sixth part of the kiln should be cylindrical except for the upper three or four courses of stonework which should draw in slightly to allow for burning away occurring principally at this level. Below the cylindrical part the kiln should diminish in size regularly to about 3ft diameter at the bottom, with two drawholes for the burnt lime to pass through. The object was for burning to take place in the upper cylindrical section, so that cooling of the lime would occur slowly as it descended in the conical part, with the pieces of lime rolling towards the sides and discharging fragmentarily rather than accumulating in a solid mass.

The kilns were fuelled with wood, peat and furze, laid alternately with layers of stone, though after the early seventeenth century coal was used. Small local sources of coal were at that time being developed, including seams in the area of Axe Edge, south-west of Buxton, and these were finding a ready market in the surrounding

A limekiln in use at Calver during the nineteenth century

lime-burning area. An inevitable result was the tendency from this time for lime-burning to become more localised and to be concentrated primarily at the points most convenient for supplies of both stone and coal, and it was probably about then that lime-burning passed from being largely a spare-time job for farmers to becoming a separate trade; numerous kilns were built of a larger type and often as adjuncts to quarries.

Though many kilns have been dismantled and the stone from their structures used for other purposes, a number of remains are still to be seen, particularly of the latter sort. An idea of the prevalence of the small agricultural kilns can be had from the earlier editions of the 6in Ordnance Survey maps on which many are marked. In some of these cases a few tumbled ruins of the kiln can be seen but more usually all that is left, if anything at all, is a mound or a few undulations. Sometimes, however, such humps and depressions are pronounced, as in the valley of the River Hamps, upstream from Onecote, where years ago limekilns dotted the hillside—about one to each farm—supplied from numerous small stonepits close by and operating until the 1880s. An example of a small double limekiln can be seen from a side road north of Flagg, at SK 127696, still in an easily recognisable state in 1970 (plate, p 35). Another of similar type, though single, with much of its stonework still intact, is in a field in Monyash parish (SK 155675). Probably in operation until 1800 it has been used as a model for an exhibit which can be seen in Derby Museum, together with another one of a larger kiln which was in existence at Newhaven, working up to the early 1800s and producing 90 tons of lime in 7 or 12 days (depending on the quality of fuel) at a cost of 10s (50p) per ton. Several examples of the remaining bigger kilns are given in the Gazetteer.

Eighteenth Century

The area's first real point of concentration of lime-burning works, and the chief one during the eighteenth century, was at Grin,

Burbage, close to Buxton whose locality, due to situation, development of communications and quality of limestone, was eventually to become a focal point of the industry. The coal seams of Axe Edge Moor were little more than a mile from the outcrop of the limestone at Grin and here during the 1700s the hill became covered with limekilns which were operated by independent lime-burners and their workers, chiefly during the summer time. Naturally, with such continued activity considerable accumulation of ash refuse from the kilns mounted up, acquiring, due to cementing qualities, a certain degree of solidity, and in these hillocks a number of poorer workers lived in caves hollowed out of the waste. Pilkington, writing in 1789, mentions ten such improvised dwellings and Farey later also refers to them.

During this century improvements were being made in transport and the network of turnpike roads was becoming developed. Buxton was finding itself well placed in relation to these, and thus with easier proximity to the bigger coalfields farther afield in Lancashire and on the east, as well as to the iron and other manufacturing concerns which, in the dawning industrial era, were seeking increased supplies of lime and limestone for their processes.

The new canal age provided a way for further expansion. On 28 March 1794 the Peak Forest Canal Company was incorporated and in the same year an Act passed for the construction of a canal and plate-way to link the Ashton-under-Lyne Canal with the Buxton limestone area. The work was carried out under Benjamin Outram and by 1799 both the canal to Bugsworth (now Buxworth) and the tramway from there to Dove Holes were in use. This provided an impetus to quarries in the Dove Holes vicinity which now became the major area of concentration.

The route of the Peak Forest Tramway, which was to remain in use for 120 years, ran from Bugsworth eastwards and south-east to Chapel-en-le-Frith, and then rose 209ft by a 512yd long inclined plane before the final stretch, graded at 1 in 200, to Dove Holes, where branches served the various quarry workings. The L-section rails were of 4ft 2½in gauge, laid on stone slabs, with stone sleepers, and though single at first, with passing places, a double track was in use by 1803. Horses, in teams of two or five, depending on the load, provided the motive power, with the inclined plane worked by gravity. The weight of descending trucks provided the power for raising those on the ascent to which they were connected originally by a hemp rope and latterly in turn by a chain and a wire rope which passed around a 10ft-diameter wheel at the top of the plane. The early waggons resembled farm carts in appearance and were made of wood, with flangeless wooden wheels hooped with wrought iron. In these the limestone and lime were carried down and coal brought up, while flat waggons were also in use for the conveyance of general provisions and agricultural goods. A rail and axle from one of the waggons can be seen in the Buxton Museum. The track of the tramway was removed in 1936 and since then most of the route sold in sections so that following it in its entirety is now impossible, but in places some of the stone sleepers can be seen and the ascending line of the inclined plane is still apparent.

Nineteenth Century

Stimulated by the new transport facilities, Dove Holes Dale in the early nineteenth century became a scene of great activity, with various new quarries being opened and older ones revived. At the same time, down along the canal banks numerous kilns sprang up, at points of convenient access for coal, and in them supplies of raw stone brought down on the tramway were calcined. In consequence, for a period up to about 1850 only very little actual limeburning was done in the Dove Holes vicinity, the main operations there being confined to quarrying. Business over these years became considerable, particularly after the opening of the Macclesfield Canal in 1830 which linked the Peak Forest Canal with the Trent & Mersey. The vast amount of industrial building going on at the time, particularly in Lancashire, called for increasing supplies of lime for mortar while demands came too from the developing chemical and other industries as well as from agriculture.

The opening in 1830–1 of the Cromford & High Peak Railway (see Chapter Seven) between Cromford and Whaley Bridge—the latter already served by an arm of the Peak Forest Canal—paved the way for further quarrying developments in the Buxton area. This time, workings on the southern side were the ones to gain advantage, including the old quarry at Grin, while others were started and intensively developed as a direct result of facilities made available by the line.

The deployment of the limestone resources on the east of Buxton was brought about by the major railway developments of the 1860s, which also provided a boost to the industry in Dove Holes Dale. In 1863 the London & North Western Company's Manchester–Whaley Bridge line reached Buxton and included a station and siding at Dove Holes. This gave the adjacent quarries a greatly improved means of transport for their material and was a factor in the re-establishment here of limeburning on an increased scale. The same year saw the opening of the Midland Railway's extension from Rowsley to Buxton, and by 1867 the continuation of the main route from Miller's Dale on this line, running right through Dove Holes Dale itself, had reached Manchester. The opening in the dale of the station known as Peak Forest obviously brought even further advantages while even more importantly, the new railway called into existence a number of further quarries in Great Rocks and Miller's Dales and along the Wye Valley close to the line to Buxton. With the Cromford & High Peak leased to the London & North Western in 1862 and control of the Peak Forest Canal Company passing to the Manchester, Sheffield & Lincolnshire Railway Company in 1863 the area was now exceptionally well served with transport facilities.

At this stage the quality and quantity of lime and limestone being demanded by rapidly growing industries could no longer be met by the less pure and smaller deposits in other formations and even in other parts of the Carboniferous Limestone outcrop. It was only in

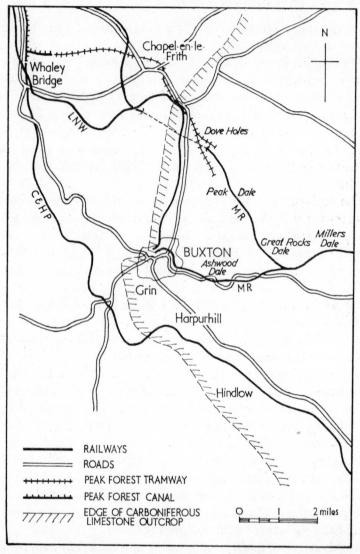

Communications in the Buxton area 1869–91. The particular development of the transport system greatly facilitated the exploitation of the exceptionally pure limestone which established Buxton as a centre of the industry

the great thicknesses of pure limestone, containing 98–99 per cent calcium carbonate and so well exposed in certain beds in this area, that suitable quarries to meet this new demand were capable of being developed. Thus the complex of limestone quarrying in the Buxton area, which had become fully established during the second half of the nineteenth century at a time when various other industries were facing economic difficulties, continued to expand. Though agriculture had reached a state of depression resulting in dwindling lime demands and the accumulation of dumps of unwanted kiln ash waste, some of which can still be seen near the road at Dove Holes and at Grin, other industries were calling for more. One of these was the steel industry in which new developments had brought increased needs for lime.

Another stimulus of considerable and increasing importance was the expanding chemical industry to the west. The manufacture of chemicals in Cheshire and south Lancashire had become established mainly due to the natural deposits of salt in the Northwich–Middlewich–Nantwich–Winsford area, known since ancient times. In 1872 it became necessary for John Brunner and Ludwig Mond, makers of soda ash—sodium carbonate, used in many industries—to cease manufacture by the old Le Blanc or sulphuric acid method as the pollution it caused was becoming ruinous to the surrounding countryside. Consequently, around 1873 the Solvay process was started at Northwich, using sodium chloride, limestone and ammonia.

Though their product was in increased demand the owners of limestone quarries in the Buxton area found problems facing them in the following years. No quarry on its own was sufficiently developed at that time to meet the rising demand for alkali stone. With the buyers eager for low prices and too many producers in competition, quarrying profits became reduced and losses hardly avoided.

The situation was remedied temporarily in 1891 with an amalgamation of quarries known as the Buxton Lime Firms Company Ltd. The concerns involved were:

Old Buxton Lime Company, Harpur Hill
Buxton Lime Company, Grin and Whaley Bridge
Buxton Central Lime & Stone Company Ltd, Blackwell
East Buxton Lime Company
Miller's Dale Lime Company
Ashwood Dale Lime & Stone Company
Great Rocks Lime & Stone Company
T. Beswick & Sons, Smalldale
Edward Heathcott & Sons, Dove Holes
Richard Briggs & Sons
J. & M. Tymm, Marple
Joseph Wainwright, Peak Dale
William Pitt Dixon, Bugsworth

The only ones in the area to remain outside the combine were four concerns in the Peak Dale–Dove Holes locality, one of them, that of Samuel Taylor at Dove Holes, being already long geared to the transport facilities of the Peak Forest Canal and Tramway and continuing so until their closure.

With demands now more easily met within the one organisation and the position of near-monopoly, prices were able to rise and become stabilised, enabling necessary improvements and modernisation to be carried out. Encouraged by the better prospects and by the opening of the London & North Western's railway from Ashbourne to Buxton in the 1890s (see Chapter Seven) the Dowlow Lime & Stone Company Ltd opened up a quarry close to Briggs's works at Hindlow, installing a Hoffman-type kiln and crushing plant, while another firm started at Brierlow with two kilns of vertical design. Brierlow was leased from 1907 to 1923 by Buxton Lime Firms who in 1908 also took over the works at Cowdale east of Buxton in King Sterndale parish, which had been opened as the New Buxton Lime Company in 1898. Subsequently this works was successfully modernised and equipped with crushing plant and four kilns of conventional design, continuing in operation until 1956.

Page 71 (right) *There are few remains today of this former comb mill at Ashford-in-the-Water. Powered by water from the River Wye, it was worked during the nineteenth century;* (below) *Alport Corn Mill on the River Lathkill. The waterwheel is on the opposite side of the building*

Page 72   (above) *Holes in this stone at Holme are one of twenty-five such pairs along a roadside wall in which tenterhooks were fixed. The tenterhooks were used for holding wool brought from a nearby mill for drying. The wooden stub of one of them can be seen in the right-hand hole;* (below) *cottages at Holme converted from buildings formerly used for woollen weaving*

1900 to Present Day

With the turn of the century advances in the industry continued, intensified by the time of World War I and after by the increased demands for roadstone and new industrial needs. In these years Brunner, Mond & Company Ltd acquired a controlling interest in the Buxton Lime Firms (which had relinquished some of its components) and together they became part of a merger which led to the formation of the Imperial Chemical Industries Ltd in 1931.

Since then some of the quarries not sold to other firms have been closed down, and at the present time operations of ICI are concentrated upon Tunstead and Hindlow. The quarry at Tunstead, formerly known as South Works, in Great Rocks Dale, has been developed since 1929 and with its $1\frac{1}{4}$ mile long, 120–200ft high face now ranks as the biggest working limestone quarry in Europe. The annual output from Tunstead is over 5 million tons of limestone, with the rock being brought down mainly by blasts of up to 60,000–70,000 tons at a time, and dealt with by highly modern plant involving three types of kiln. The limestone is of exceptionally high purity of 98 per cent calcium carbonate and is thus well suited to the needs of the firm's Cheshire alkali works to which a third of the production travels by rail in specially designed high-capacity wagons. In addition, considerable quantities are used for roadstone and concrete aggregates, while the bulk of the quicklime from the kilns is absorbed by the iron and steel industries, the rest being used by other industries, the building trade and in such processes as water purification and oil refining. Hydrated lime is also produced, chiefly for building purposes, while by-products formerly wasted are now utilised in the making of cement.

Only two of the original Buxton Lime Firms' quarries lie actually within the boundary of the national park and both are now disused. One is that of the East Buxton Lime Works (SK 133732) in Wormhill parish, north of the railway line near the former Miller's Dale station, which closed down finally in 1944. The other, the former Miller's

E

Dale Limeworks, south of the railway at Oldham sidings, Taddington parish (SK 143732), was opened in 1878 and closed in 1930; the considerable remains, including those of buildings and the chute system, as well as kilns, form an impressive sight from the other side of the valley (plate, p 53).

Outside the national park boundary the Buxton Lime Firms' large quarry at Harpur Hill was the site of a very big Hoffman kiln which was something of an innovation when constructed in 1872. Oval in shape, it remained in continuous use until closed down by ICI in 1944; in 1951 its tall chimney was demolished and now only the partial walls remain (plate, p 53). Other kilns of some antiquity which were also operated in their later days by ICI were four open-top shaft kilns at the Perseverance Works in Peak Dale (SK 086771), built under Messrs Bibbington in 1847 and served by an independent siding from the Peak Forest Tramway. Burning a mixture of coke and coal, their use was abandoned in 1939 (plate, p 36).

Of course, though the historic factors already described together with the exceptionally high purity of the resources of limestone have made the Buxton area the chief concentration of the continuing industry, limestone quarrying has also been of considerable importance elsewhere, both within the national park and beyond, particularly in the Matlock and Wirksworth areas, with numerous concerns catering on a large scale for the ever increasing demands of roadmaking and industry. Such quarries within the park are those at Topley Pike (Taddington), Eldon Hill (Peak Forest), Ballidon, Shining Bank (Alport) and Grangemill, all developed comparatively recently in times when improved road transport facilities have freed quarrying of its dependence on railway alignment. Another notable area of production is at Stoney Middleton where earlier quarrying and lime-burning activities have been intensively developed in recent years. And at Hope the quarrying of limestone is combined with the extraction of shale for making cement.

Reference to numerous disused quarries in the district is included in the Gazetteer.

'MARBLE'

At Ashford-in-the-Water and in some other places the extraction and working of marble was an important local industry for a period of about 200 years. Not actually marble in the true geological sense, the substance is in fact an impure form of limestone, usually dark grey, but becoming black in colour and highly decorative when polished.

Evidently known in prehistoric times—a dressed slab was found in a tumulus on the hill north of Ashford called Fin Cop—the marble was certainly being worked around 1690 when it was mentioned in some Chatsworth accounts. In 1748 Henry Watson established his marble mill at Ashford (SK 190694) and the material was used for a wide variety of ornamental purposes including interior building work —particularly at Chatsworth—and in the making of such things as table tops, statues, vases and trinkets. The chief source of the marble was the Arrock Quarry (SK 191694), now overgrown, fenced off and dangerous, a short distance from the A6 on the minor road to Sheldon. Originally quarried, and later mined underground, the blocks were taken across the river to the mill where, by the use of water power, the marble was sawn to the required shapes, ground and polished. In 1832, some years after Watson's death in 1786 which preceded several changes of hands, a mine was opened by a Mr Oldfield across the valley in the Rookery Plantation (SK 190695) and marble extracted here from deep inside the hillside also supplied to the mill.

After 1835 the craft advanced to inlay work in geometric and floral designs, for which other varieties and kindred substances from different parts of the neighbouring district and elsewhere were employed. Rosewood marble, whitish in colour but banded with reddish brown when polished (due to the presence of iron oxide) was brought from nearby Nettler Dale, and the rare duke's red marble, found in an unrecorded and reputedly now-exhausted source in a mine at Alport, was also used. Others included a bird's-eye marble from Wetton and a mottled grey from Monyash. Barytes—brown from near Arbor Low a few miles to the south-west, white and pink from Castleton, Bradwell and Sheldon—was another substance used in the inlaying as also was blue john, for which Watson was a pioneer of the mine at Castleton, as already described. Etching and engraving of the marble were further artistic developments but these appear to have had only limited popularity.

The middle years of the nineteenth century were the busiest with the mines in full production and material being supplied to the numerous marble workers and inlayers of Ashford who operated in their homes, as well to workshops at Matlock, Bakewell, Buxton and Castleton. With Buxton and Matlock having become fashionable health resorts the products enjoyed a ready sale and countless examples found their way in visitors' homeward luggage to far distant places.

There was also a marble works at Bakewell, east of the river downstream from the bridge (SK 220686) where the buildings still remain adjoining the present sawmill. The widow of J. Thorp, a marble mason, sold them in 1742 to Henry Watson of Ashford who commenced business here in 1751. In the mid-nineteenth century they were operated by John Lomas who in 1847 was also leasing from the Duke of Rutland a black marble quarry at Blackstone Hollow (SK 200678) below Green Cowden.

Towards the end of the century, however, interest declined and the industry suffered from the competition of other materials. Though turbines had been installed during the later years, marble working at the Ashford mill ceased in 1905. For a number of years afterwards the premises were used as a barytes mill by the Via Gellia Colour Company, and then for timber; part of the site was later absorbed in the construction of the A6 road and the remainder, with the greater part of the buildings now demolished, is a depot of the North Derbyshire Water Board. A dwindling amount of inlay work from reserves of the material still in hand continued in certain places for a number of years after closure of the mill.

IGNEOUS ROCKS

Basalt, the igneous rock produced by volcanic outpourings during the limestone's formation, often found as a barrier to the continuation of lead veins, was well known to the lead miner who called it toadstone, probably a corruption of the term *todstein* meaning dead stone, used by German miners. Found outcropping at points along a line between Dove Holes and Matlock this very hard substance occurs interbedded with the limestone or as intrusive masses of later age which cut across the bedding. It is also found as the plug of an actual extinct volcano at Calton Hill Quarry, in Blackwell parish (SK 119715) where from 1906 to 1969 it was worked for use as roadstone. An old quarry in Tideswell Dale, on the boundary of Tideswell and Litton parishes (SK 154738), now owned by the Peak Park Planning Board and adapted as a picnic place, was worked for basalt prior to World War II, and one at Ible (SK 253567) was in similar production until the earlier years of this century; a reservoir was constructed above it to provide power for working the crushers, and loading was done via chutes at the roadside below.

An intrusive dolerite is currently worked for roadstone and precast concrete products at Waterswallows Quarry, Green Fairfield, just outside the park boundary.

CHERT

Chert, a hard, siliceous flint-like material, occurs in the higher beds of the limestone outcrop. It has been extracted from pits west of Great Longstone and in a small quarry at Ashford (SK 193695) but the main workings have been in the Bakewell locality from where, in the eighteenth century, chert was being taken to Staffordshire and Yorkshire for the making of earthenware. Blocks of chert were used in the Potteries for the grinding of calcined flint, used with the clay in manufacture as a whitening agent.

Up to 1772 coloured granite stones had been used for the grinding, which was done not by the potters themselves but by outside milling agencies which supplied them with the ground flint in slurry form. In April 1772 it was written that Josiah Wedgwood 'recommends the use of Derbyshire Chert in place of blue Granites or Boulders as we call them, it answers very well and avoids the black specks in our body'. At a meeting of the 'Club of Potters' held in Hanley in the same year Wedgwood recommended: 'We shall abolish grinding it [calcined flint] with coloured Granite and make trials of a stone called Chert which is found in abundance near Bakewell, Derbyshire' and he requested that they should 'send Mr Sherrat to order a quantity'.[1]

The chert was originally carried by packhorse or carted by road the whole distance to the Potteries, but after 1793 the blocks went by road only as far as Cromford and from there to their destination by canal; later they were sent by rail.[2]

Holme Bank Quarry (SK 213692) is the older of the two known sources of chert at Bakewell and it was being extracted here by means of tunnels in the rock for use in the Potteries and also for poultry grit until a few years ago. The other source, Pretoria Quarry, on the Monyash road (SK 210681) was opened in the early 1900s and was also worked by mining underground but, since 1969, this too has been closed.

POCKET SILICAS

The deposits known as pocket silicas, consisting of sands, clays and quartzite pebbles, occur in a band about 5 miles wide extending roughly from Parsley Hay to Brassington. The material is of much later origin than the limestone into which it settled in spaces as 'pockets' or 'pipes', these being exposed at the surface by subsequent glacial action which left them in a form somewhat similar to that of a sliced-off boiled egg. The silicas are currently worked and used in manufacture at Friden by DSF Refractories Ltd and also at Brassington (outside the park) by the Steetley Company Ltd.

As in numerous other places, there was probably a small brick-making industry already in existence at Friden, and the heat resistant qualities of the silica well known, when John West founded the original company in 1892. He and his co-founders were gas engineers, their object being to manufacture an improved type of siliceous product suitable for the gas industry and, using material entirely from their own sources, they developed a high-quality refractory brick of a type which continued to be made up to 1855. From that time, due to its changing methods, the gas industry's requirements of these materials became less, and today are practically negligible. But in the 1920s the manufacture of refractories for the steel trade had commenced and in addition to using their own siliceous substances the company had started bringing in quartzite rocks and importing materials from abroad. This procedure has continued and increased and today only 40 per cent of the tonnage used is local production.

At one stage surrounding land owned by the company amounted to around 1,000 acres but the greater part has been gradually sold off as redundant and now only a small acreage is retained, though some land is leased in other areas. Working has been in opencast pits, usually of 80–100ft in depth and sometimes more, back-filled with waste on becoming worked out. The present areas of working are at Kenslow and Heathcote.

The main transport facilities in the earlier days were provided by the Cromford & High Peak Railway to which the Friden works was aligned with its own siding. In addition the dispersal of the various pits necessitated the company having its own transport system of tramways. There were originally about 12 miles of these reaching out from the works and although the rails have now been removed from all but the 1 mile remaining in use, and the routes absorbed into the agricultural land, their lines can in some cases still be detected, particularly with the aid of a map. Of 2ft gauge, the system was single track throughout with passing places, either as loops or shunting bays, about every ¼ mile. Horses provided the motive power in the earlier days, each drawing two 25cwt waggons; they became very

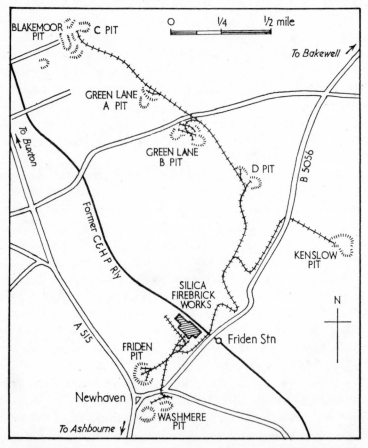

Routing of the tramways which served the silica pits and firebrick works at Friden

used to the procedure and would work unled, with a brakesman riding on the waggon and operating the brake with his feet. Eventually a change was made to tractor power and in 1922 diesel locomotives were introduced. Later in the 1920s the company had six Simplex locomotives in operation and in 1937 the first of six Rustons—particularly suited on account of their stability and tolerance of irregularities in the track—was in use, with each locomotive drawing six waggons at a time. Up to World War II all transport from the pits to the works was by the tramways and by horses and drays, but in 1946, with the material from Blakemoor pits taking an hour in transit, it was realised that the method was too slow and since then haulage from the pits has been by lorries.

MILLSTONE GRIT

The Millstone Grit Series which surrounds the central dome of the Carboniferous Limestone on three sides consists of a series of sandstones interbedded with shales, varying in texture from a coarse grit to a fine-grained sandstone and in form from a massive to a thin lamellar structure. At the edges of the plateaux formed by the different layers the gritstone outcrops vertically—marking the extent of the central area of denudation—and in some places has been extracted. Unlike limestone, millstone grit is of only limited economic importance today but in the past it has been valued and worked for a variety of purposes.

Millstones

A very ancient use of millstone grit, as the name suggests, was in the making of millstones. Already utilised for the small hand mills or querns used for grinding corn and other substances, the rock undoubtedly provided material for the stones of the earliest corn mills, of which there were a number in existence by early Norman times, and Peak millstones became well known in many different parts of the country.

Though various places have been the scene of millstone making, including the slopes of Kinder Scout, the beds of rock known as the Chatsworth or Rivelin Grits, forming one of the middle layers of the Millstone Grit Series and ranging in depth from 60–150ft, are particularly well suited for the purpose and have been those most exploited. A series of edges running northwards from Gardom's Edge (east of Baslow), including those of Baslow, Curbar, Froggatt, Millstone and Stanage, are amongst those which consist of this type of rock and at numerous places along the slopes immediately beneath them many examples of millstones left in various stages of completion still remain (plate, p 54). Most of these were undoubtedly discarded due to some flaw or imperfection in the stone, or perhaps to a human error in handling, though some probably owe their abandonment to the eventual fall in demand which caused reserve stocks to remain unused.

Considerable industry in this field is evident from the number and variation in size of these remains. Stones found appear to be of either an earlier type, probably dating from not later than the early nineteenth century, often now clothed with lichen and partly covered by scrub and vegetation, or of later origin, newer in appearance and seemingly the more numerous.

The older sort, of 6–7ft diameter, are comparatively thin, many of them being about 12in deep in the centre and tapering to a rounded edge. They have been found to bear different inscriptions according to the area of their origin and some have holes in the centre, some not. Though their occurrence is fairly general along the edges already mentioned the greatest number have been found in the vicinity of Gardom's Edge where the rock has been quarried at five points and where there are signs of seven main working areas below. The later stones are generally cylindrical and thicker than the others in relation to their diameter which may vary from around 3ft to over 7ft 6in. Working of these seems to have been concentrated in fewer areas than the older kind with that of Stanage Edge predominant.

Extraction of rock for the millstones has apparently been both by digging out of the ground, as at Stanage, and in other places by quarrying; hammers, chisels and wedges being used. It seems that the rough blocks were formed first into hexagons and then, while resting on a pedestal of stone, the circular shape and flat surface gradually achieved by careful trimming, first on one side and then on the other with the central hole made last. Methods of transport are uncertain; the stones would have been too heavy for packhorses though they may have been drawn by sledges. It seems likely, however, that in the earliest days the millstones travelled to their destinations in pairs, joined at their centres by 'axles' of wood and rolled on their circumferences like wheels. Later they were doubtless moved by waggon. In each case working areas were served by trackways, their courses still apparent, connecting them with the main routes or turnpike system.

Besides their function in corn mills the stones were used for crushing rape, pulping wood, in the making of paint, and also, as described in Chapter Two, in the crushing of lead ore. In some cases they were employed for crushing stone to sand, as at a small quarry at Sandmill Hollow, south of Chunal (Charlesworth) where an old millstone reputedly formerly used for the purpose lies to the east of the A624 road, beside the Grouse Inn (SK 033905). Millstone grit was utilised too for making such items of equipment as water troughs and cheese presses. Farey (1815) quotes current prices of millstones made in the Hathersage area as being 10 guineas for a pair of 5ft diameter, 12 guineas for 5ft 4in and 14 guineas for 5ft 8in, with smaller stones of 4ft 6in for paint grinding or for exportation fetching 8 guineas. (One guinea equals £1.05.)

As far as grinding corn was concerned Peak millstones were used more for oats and barley than for the production of flour from wheat. Generally, and particularly from the eighteenth century, stones of a different nature were used for wheat grinding, corn mills usually operating both kinds. Besides those made in other parts of Britain, Black Rhenish lava millstones were imported from the Continent in early times for milling wheat, and later, sectional ones made of chert were brought in from France.

In 1862 England's first roller mills for grinding corn were built and from then on the demand for millstones gradually diminished. Probably the last area to be concerned was that around Hathersage though it is impossible to say exactly when the trade finally ceased. When the Millstone Quarries, as part of the Longshaw Estate, were bought by Sheffield Corporation in 1927, one of the six (out of the original eight) faces being leased was tenanted by the firm of W. J. & J. Child, still listed in 1928 as 'millstone makers', but it seems that in the latter days whatever stone was extracted for millstone making was taken away and worked to shape elsewhere.

Grindstones

Stone from Derbyshire has been used for the making of grindstones, whetstones and hones for over three centuries, in the Peak District that part of the succession known as the Kinderscout Grit being particularly suitable. In addition to supplying needs throughout the country the material has been of considerable importance to the cutlery and other metal industries of nearby Sheffield, where stones of different sizes and textures have long been employed for various abrasive purposes. Large ones, of 6ft diameter, have been used in the making of saws—being often assigned to other sections of the industry on becoming reduced in size with wear—and others of smaller dimensions for such purposes as file grinding and sharpening and for the other different types of articles being produced.

Farey records three places in the Peak District where grindstones were being made in the early nineteenth century: Mossylee (east of Glossop), Beeley Moor and Stanton-in-the-Peak. The blocks of stone were chipped out in rough octagonal form and then apparently worked down and rounded by abrasive action applied by women and boys.

In the nineteenth century the industry was in decline against the more extensive use of stones from other areas, and in 1900 the introduction of other substances as more reliable abrasives brought almost complete demise. Today, however, a limited number of grindstones are still being made, chiefly for export. From Stoke Quarry (SK 236769) near Grindleford, they are sent to the United States—for use in grinding cork—and to Sweden; and from the Watts Cliff Quarry, Elton (SK 221621), grindstones also go to America, as well as to other places including Ghana. At the quarries and works of Ann Twyford Ltd at Stanton and Birchover grindstones are prepared and exported to various parts of the world for such purposes as glass bevelling and the sharpening of knives for sugar cane, and large stones for crushing wood to pulp for papermaking are sent to Scandinavia and America. In past days Twyfords made stones extensively for Sheffield hand-grinders—stacking them at Rowsley station for dispatch by rail—and also supplied metal works in Birmingham and the Black Country. The firm still continues to provide for file-grinding requirements in Sheffield, supplying stones of 2ft 6in–4ft 8in diameter, 12in in depth.

Building Material

As a building material millstone grit has a long tradition and high reputation. Comparatively easily dressed, the Kinderscout Grit with its high bulk and strength is specially well suited for heavy construction work and it is this type which has been most extensively, though not exclusively, used for the purpose. Parishes in the gritstone area, eg Pilsley and Abney, Holme, Hayfield and Hathersage, with houses some hundreds of years old, bear witness to the stone's long established use for domestic building, the light sandy colour weathering to more sombre tones with prolonged exposure to the atmosphere, appearing outwardly austere yet evoking a sense of secure stability and a suggested warmth within, perfectly inherent to the surrounding countryside.

Not only for the walls of houses has millstone grit been used but also for such parts as window frames and mullions, door jambs and lintels, to which its dressing potentialities lend themselves. Even in the limestone area, gritstone has often been employed for these items, as well as for quoins. In addition certain flat beds of the rock, yielding stone in thin layers of varying thickness, have long provided a convenient material for roofing tiles, flag stones and outdoor paving slabs; while stone cleared from the ground, or quarried, has been used for building boundary walls and for gateposts—the latter not only here but frequently also on the limestone.

With the industrial advances of the last two centuries millstone grit became increasingly sought after for more massive structures. The stone was employed for mill building both in the cloughs of the Peak District itself and in the growing manufacturing areas beyond, and for erecting public edifices of sufficient grandiosity to be deemed worthy of the newly acquired status of developing towns, as well as for kerb stones and setts for paving their streets. Meanwhile the spread of the railways absorbed huge quantities of millstone grit, solid and reliable for the building of arches and viaducts, and the making of reservoirs and construction of dams brought demands which have intensified during the present century.

Besides the use of massive blocks and freestone, some of the thin lamellar gritstones have been utilised for purposes calling for properties of heat resistance. One of these has been the making of pye or pot stones, round plates about an inch thick and 9 or 10in in diameter used in iron forges for heating pieces of metal for the tilt hammers; the quarries at Spout House, Bradfield, are quoted by Farey as a place where this was done. Another purpose, using somewhat larger stones of the same type, was the making of bakestones used by housewives for cooking their oatcakes. These were either thin and round for use on a hanging trivet suspended from a pot-hook over the fire—usually in cottages—or larger and square for placing on top of a stove. Farey mentions Beeley, Birchover Moor and Crookstone peat pits near Rowlee on the moors north of Hope, as sources of these, while Bakestonedale, Pott Shrigley, where they were also produced, is reputedly so named from being thus associated.

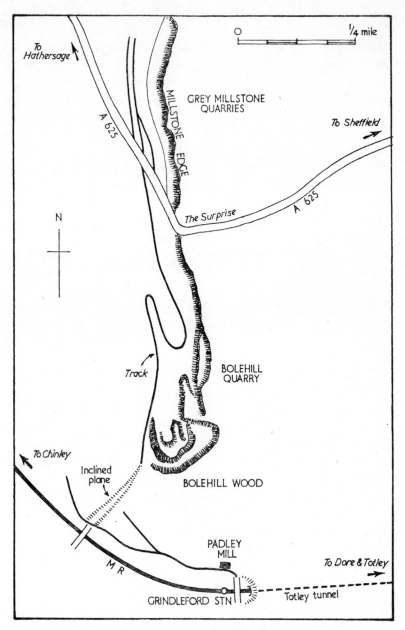

The Millstone and Bolehill quarries

Of the many gritstone quarries to be seen in the gritstone country-side a number are old parish quarries, used, like similar ones in the limestone area, as sources of stone for local requirements since early days. Others have served wider needs chiefly in more recent times, some of them leaving remains that are impressive. These include the Glossop Low Quarries (SK 058961) closed at the end of the nine-teenth century, and Cracken Edge Quarry on the eastern slopes of Chinley Churn (SK 037836, etc) which was worked until the late 1920s, the better stone at greater depth being extracted by under-ground mining into the top of the hill. Besides yielding building stone both these quarries specialised in the production of paving flags and roofing slates. Farey records that paviers from Glossop Low were sold squared at 1s (5p) to 1s 4d per yard super—3d a yard more, according to grade, when brought down to the town—and that slates from the same source, sufficient for a rood of slating or 44 sq yd, fetched 52s (£2·6) at the quarry, 64s (£3·2) in the town. Both paving and roofing slates were also produced at the Goytsclough Quarry in Hartington Upper Quarter (SK 011734) first worked by Thomas Pickford in the seventeenth century and later leased by Pickford to Richard Wilson, stone from which was used in the paving of London's Regent Street. At one stage there were proposals to construct a canal to serve the quarry, and also a railway from near Leek, but neither materialised. In Farey's time the quarry was run by a Mr Joseph Marchington and either then or later an enormous waterwheel was employed to power apparatus for scouring and smoothing the stone. This, reputed to have been one of the largest in the world, was in position until the end of the nineteenth century.

The Millstone Quarries (SK 248800–248808) have already been referred to as a source of material for millstones, but they were also notable for the production of building stone. This has been used locally, as in Hathersage Church, and in more distant places including Liverpool where it features in St George's Hall. Standing high above Hathersage and the Derwent Valley, the quarried edge is imposing when viewed from a distance, and awe-inspiring at close range. Less

Page 89   (above) *New or Arkwright's Square, Bakewell, built by Arkwright for his cotton-mill workers in the late eighteenth century. The arched entry gives access to the inner courtyard;* (below) *Brund Mill, Sheen, which bears the date 1762. Powered by the River Manifold the mill was used at different times for cotton and corn*

Page 90   (above) *The Georgian-style cotton-mill building at Cressbrook which was added to earlier structures in 1815;* (below) *Edale Mill, used for cotton manufacture until 1934*

easily seen by travellers on the Sheffield road as they turn the corner at the Surprise are the Bole Hill Quarries (SK 249795) situated on the continuation of Millstone Edge south of the road. One and a quarter million tons of stone from here were used in the construction of the Howden and Derwent dams in the early years of the present century (see Chapter Five), being conveyed by rail from the station at Grindleford, to which the quarries were connected by an inclined plane. Near the quarry faces the stone was loaded into rail trucks, some with high sides for smaller material and others flat for carrying large blocks, and drawn by locomotives along rail tracks to the top of the plane (plate, p 54). The full trucks descended by gravity controlled by cables winding over drums at the top, with empty ones being raised simultaneously by their weight. Rails on the plane were of standard gauge, and the stone travelled in the same trucks throughout the journey, three consignments usually being dispatched along the system each day. The inclined plane is now largely overgrown but its lower part can be easily seen in the form of a cutting passing beneath the lane at Upper Padley (SK 246790); near this point there were formerly joinery and blacksmith's shops and sleeping huts for men working on the project. Above, the Bole Hill Quarries remain now silent and deserted, gently wooded with silver birch trees, the haunt of green woodpeckers. The area is now owned by the National Trust and is easily entered by a grassy path from near the Surprise viewpoint. Alongside this path around 200 small-size millstones lie, stacked and abandoned since the end of the last century.

In later years there has been a considerable decline in the quarrying of millstone grit due to the development of new methods of construction and of more cheaply produced materials, and only a few gritstone quarries still operate in the national park. In addition to the continued limited making of grindstones already mentioned, a certain amount of building stone for specific requirements is still produced, including stone for new and repair work on buildings and also for such purposes as the construction of domestic fireplaces, with the introduction of stone cutting machinery having simplified the process

F

of earlier days. Crushed stone is also used to an extent for pitching, while small waste is utilised in the making of artificial stone for building purposes.

COAL

Isolated patches of the Lower Coal Measures occur at points near the eastern and western boundaries of the national park which in the past have been mined in a small way for the production of coal. Though generally of a rather low, sulphurous quality the coal found a ready use locally, particularly before the opening of the railways which made superior supplies more easily available. In most cases working ceased by around 1900, but in some places has taken place in the present century, particularly in times of national emergency.

Extraction was achieved both by shafts and by means of tunnels or adits into a hillside and often there is little to be seen now at these various sites of coal mining other than general disturbance of the ground. On the eastern side coal was mined in the Bradfield area—near the Strines Inn and near Ughill (resorted to at the time of the General Strike in 1926); at Salter Sitch west of Owler Bar; east of Baslow near Robin Hood; and on Beeley Moor. On the west, in the area of New Mills there were mines on the hills around Rowarth; continuing southwards, there were others at Pott Shrigley, where a number of shafts and 'day-eye' pits (a name given to those entered horizontally from the hillside) are still visible on the moorland above Bakestonedale. Coal was mined here from the end of the eighteenth century and further developed during the second half of the nineteenth to serve the local brickmaking industry. Early this century Bakestonedale coal was being supplied to local inhabitants at 4d per cwt. Coal mines in the vicinity of Rainow included one on the hillside at Harrop, worked in the last century by Joseph Jodrell and his son Caleb, and at times in the present one until the mine flooded in 1934. On Goyt's Moss and Axe Edge, south-west of Buxton, coal was mined both for domestic purposes and, as already mentioned, for use in limeburning. There were a number of workings in Wildboarclough parish—at Knar, Holt (where an old chimney stack still stands) and at Cumberland. Still farther south, in Quarnford, coal was mined on Goldsitch Moss, while in Leekfrith flooded open shafts near Hazel Barrow still remain from operations which finished at the end of the nineteenth century.

FIRECLAY

Also occurring in the Lower Coal Measures are deposits of siliceous fireclays which have been extracted for the making of firebricks and glazed ware on account of their high heat-resistant properties. The clays have been worked in three main locations in the national park area—at Meltham, Bradfield and Pott Shrigley.

The Meltham workings were on Royd Edge, started with the founding of the Meltham Silica Firebrick Company Ltd in 1900 because of the occurrence of quartzite rock. The gannister was used successfully for the manufacture of most types of silica bricks until about 1954 when tighter specifications in the industry called for a higher standard of raw material and as a result General Refractories Ltd—the controlling firm since 1934—closed down the Royd Edge Quarries in 1966.

Gannister has also been extracted in Bradfield parish, for example near Loadfield. The present concentration of fireclay working at Bradfield is, however, in the locality of Ughill, where pot or crucible clay is mined from beds 4–10ft thick, by both underground and opencast methods, for use in the making of heat-resistant bricks and moulds for the steel industry. Underground methods predominated in earlier days, mainly by drifts into the hillsides and by vertical shafts on Furnace Hill and, from old drifts discovered during later opencast operations, it seems likely that some workings may date from the eighteenth century. A former employee, now in his eighties, whose father and grandfather also previously worked in these mines, remembers the shafts on Furnace Hill, 32yd deep, being worked at the turn of the century by a horse-operated winch. The clay was extracted by pick, hammer and wedge—explosives were in use later— and was in three grades: black clay which was ground for different fireclay purposes; pot clay; and a light, white or yellow coloured variety used for making bricks for furnace linings. Today, less costly, small-scale opencast methods are employed for extraction of the clay, which is sent to works in the Loxley Valley (outside the national park) for manufacture.

At Pott Shrigley fireclay described as 'bastard silica' was extracted from the hillsides of Bakestonedale from about 1820 until recent years. Originally white glazed tiles were made with the material in works north of the Pott Shrigley–Kettleshulme road, but, after a fire, production from around 1900 was concentrated on the making of firebricks and furnace linings in the premises on the south side, continuing under Messrs William Hammond Ltd until 1967.

Notes to this chapter are on page 249

CHAPTER FOUR

Mills and Manufacturing

CORN MILLS AND OTHERS

Corn Mills

CORN mills have been a feature of the countryside for several hundreds of years and the Peak District, with arable farming practised more generally in the past than now, has had an ample share. In this part of the country, with its hills and valleys and abundant supplies of running water, the vast majority of corn mills were water mills, indications of windmills being few. Probably the last of the few windmills that did exist was at Eyam (SK 213766); apparently of the tower type, it was demolished before 1877 after long being in disuse. The name, Windmill, of a hamlet in the parish of Little Hucklow is suggestive of one having been there, obviously an advantageous site for wind prospects, but no definite evidence is available.

Just when water mills were first introduced to supersede the hand querns of former days is not known, though it is thought possible that the first ones in this country were built in the late fourth or early fifth centuries AD, during the latter years of the Roman occupation. Between five and six thousand were recorded in the Domesday survey, completed in 1086, which included a number in the Peak District. Naturally enough, there are no remains today of these early buildings, although, while the original precise sites are not known, it is reasonable to suppose that where mills exist in places which had them at the time of Domesday, the present ones most probably occupy the same stream-side situations as their predecessors. Though mill buildings, subject to wear and tear from vibration and general use, had to be rebuilt from time to time, there would have been no need to alter the particular system of weirs, pool and leats as already installed and which, properly maintained, could serve a succession of buildings.

Bakewell is an example of a place shown in Domesday Book as having a water mill. Valued at 10s 8d (53½p) it must have been of fair size by comparison with one at nearby Ashford, valued at only 12d (5p). Both these places still have mill buildings (described, as are others, in the Gazetteer) fed by the River Wye and standing on sites which must surely have been as favourable in the eleventh century as in more recent days. Alport Mill (Harthill parish) is another known to be of early origin and could well be the one of 5s 4d (26½p) value included under Youlgreave. Under the manorial system tenants were obliged to grind their corn at the manor mill, where one existed, a system which assured the landowner of a steady source of income and which was generally unpopular with the tenants. The millers, in their extraction of toll taken as a portion of the flour, often took more than they should and as characters they were frequently disliked.

Altogether over fifty corn mills are known to have existed in the area covered by the national park, with just over a third of the parishes being represented and a few having had more than one. The mills are found in relation to both the limestone and gritstone areas, though often in their valley situations the actual mills themselves stand on the shales.

From the total number, all that can be seen of about 16 is the site and usually the weir and traces of the leat system, or minimal building remains, several of the structures having been demolished for the re-use of their stone. Approximately 7 former mills remain as derelict buildings while around the same number are now adapted for housing livestock or for other agricultural purposes. At least 4—1 at Hartington, 1 at Hope and 2 at Hathersage—have been converted to dwelling houses. In 4 cases former mills have evolved into present-day factories, while out of all these groups 5 early corn mills were the sites of later mills for wool or cotton prior to their current respective uses or disuse.

Five mills are still in use either for grinding corn or for kindred storage purposes. Those at Rowsley and Ashford-in-the-Water both continue milling by water power, but using turbines instead of the former waterwheels. Meanwhile the mills at Brough, Alport and Miller's Dale (Wormhill)—all ancient ones—are now used as depots by firms supplying agricultural feeding stuffs.

Paper Mills

Paper mills have existed at certain places, sited often remotely, where suitable streams could provide power for pulping and clear water for the manufacturing process. Possibly the oldest of them was one known to have existed three centuries ago near Youlgreave, on the left bank of the River Lathkill just above Alport Bridge, but no signs of it remain. Another no longer visible was in the Longdendale Valley north-east of Glossop at Torside; this was in operation in 1811 but by 1850 production had apparently ceased, part of the premises being then in use as a public house, and very soon afterwards the mill became submerged beneath the waters of the Torside Reservoir. A short distance from it, at the foot of Fair Vage Clough (SK 079990), there still stands the gaunt shell of another long-disused paper mill beside the swift stream by which it was formerly powered.

Just over a mile north of Hathersage in Outseats parish are some interesting remains of an old paper mill in an isolated situation (SK 233837). Known as Green's House Paper Mill it was occupied by Charles Marsden 'manufacturer of coarse brown paper' in 1857 but production ceased long before the end of the century. Parts of the walls of the buildings remain on level ground beside the stream, one having covered an area of approximately 40 × 20ft. On a higher level, behind an apparently natural dam, is the millpond, still holding water fed by springs above and discharging to the stream, with grooves for the sluices still visible. A stream of water continues to fall beside walling where the waterwheel was situated.

Some ruinous remains are all that is left of Folly Mill, near Allgreave (SJ 971664), one of two paper mills which formerly existed in Wincle parish. The original mill here was probably built by Abraham Day in about 1790 but it is believed that the present remains are of the third, three-storeyed, mill which he built on the site, the first and second buildings having been washed away by floods. According to tradition his wife told him it would be 'folly' to build a third and that if he did so she would go to bed and never get up again. Heedlessly Day persisted with his intention and, true to her word, his wife retired to bed so it is said, and stayed there until she died in 1826 aged 76. Another theory about the mill's name concerns its remoteness and inaccessibility for raw materials—Day's choice of site, deep in the valley of the Clough Brook, a tributary of the Dane, was locally considered 'folly'—and it is noteworthy that when the mill was advertised for letting in 1849 'with water power and machinery for finishing paper' it was thought prudent to amend the name to Folly Grove Paper Mill. The mill was used for the manufacture of coarse brown or blue paper of the type used in the past by grocers and ironmongers and though apparently worked originally by Day himself, in 1825 was being operated by Thomas Hope of White Lee, who also ran the other Wincle paper mill. This stood some way downstream, on the Cheshire side of the river opposite Gighall, but has long since vanished.

Also in existence in 1857 was a paper mill at Rowarth, near New Mills, but this has disappeared. At Hayfield, however, a paper mill at Bank Vale (SK 031875), which was being worked in the early nineteenth century, is now modernised and still functions under Messrs John Slack Ltd.

Timber and Bone Grinding Mills

Mills for timber and for grinding bones are others which have used Peak District water power. The corn mill at Rowsley already referred to as being still in use, is said to have been formerly used for timber, as also at one time was Brund Mill, Sheen (SK 099613). In the Staffordshire parish of Heaton there are the remains of Bearda Saw

Mill (SJ 964640), which was powered by a tributary of the River Dane; though not used for many years the large area of the mill-pond, now weed grown, with the sluices is still clearly apparent and some remains of machinery lie in what was the wheelpit. Still standing is the building of a former saw mill in the village of Bradwell (SK 174811), where the waterwheel was driven by the Bradwell Brook; this wheel was removed earlier this century but the site of the sluices can be determined.

Other saw mills which have been in later use include one on the site of the former marble works at Ashford-in-the-Water (SK 190694) in operation in the 1930s, and the timber works of Messrs R. Smith & Sons by the River Wye at Bakewell (SK 220685) which continues to function, though the water turbines which are still in existence have not been used for some years. One which is still in use and actually employing a waterwheel for powering timber saws is Longnor Mill, situated by the River Manifold in the parish of Heathylee (SK 085646). This mill seems to have had a varied history. It is believed originally to have been a corn mill, later used for grinding bones, and in the 1930s was the scene of a fire. Wooden hay racks were made in more recent years and the premises are now used as a saw mill by the Harpur Crewe estate, the present owners; the over-shot waterwheel, of approximately 14ft 6in diameter, 5ft 6in wide, has wooden spokes and iron buckets.

According to Farey, bones from London and elsewhere were brought to Derbyshire to be crushed for manure, and one place he mentions where this was done was Ashford. Two mill buildings still remain at the site (Sheldon parish, SK 182696) with two iron water-wheels still in position on either side of one of them, power having been provided by the River Wye. In later times these premises too were used for timber.

Comb Mills

The making of combs was also done in small water mills at the end of the nineteenth century. Meadows & Company occupied a former cotton mill at Stretfield, Brough (SK 178820), for this purpose for a few years, using cow-horn as their material, and at Ashford-in-the-Water Rowland Holmes made combs from tortoiseshell in a small mill constructed as a secondary user of the marble mill leat (plate, p 71). Some ruins of this building remain adjoining the site of the former marble works, slightly downstream (SK 190694).

Colour Grinding Mills

Another use of water power was for grinding material for paint. A mill which existed at Goytsclough (SK 012733), close to the quarry and powered by water from the stream in Deep Clough, is reputed to have been latterly used for this purpose before its closure many years ago and subsequent demolition. Near Chapel-en-le-Frith, at SK 073798 across the road from the route of the Peak Forest Tramway, is the site of an old works where barytes was ground for paint-making; the former Lord, Smelt Mill at Stoney Middleton was converted to a barytes mill, as already mentioned (Chapter Two), and the same process was carried on for a number of years after 1905 at the former Ashford marble mill. The firm concerned at Ashford was the Via Gellia Colour Company Ltd whose works in Bonsall Dale (SK 278573), formerly used for lead smelting, may have been a colour grinding mill referred to by Farey as being in existence in the early nineteenth century.

Gunpowder Mill

Gunpowder was also made with the aid of water power at a mill which existed for many years in the Goyt Valley at Fernilee, the remains of which now lie submerged by the reservoir. It is believed to have been in existence as early as the sixteenth century and according to local tradition supplied powder for the defeat of the Spanish Armada. In 1857 the mill was in the hands of Thomas

Williamson and the last owner, before closure after World War I, was the Chilworth Gunpowder Company. The process of grinding and combining the ingredients of charcoal, sulphur and saltpetre to make the black powder was carried out in buildings of massive structure and strength which, with others used for storage, defied to the last the eventual efforts to demolish them by blasting. A hundred men were employed at the works at one stage. Naturally, work with this highly explosive substance was dangerous, and frequent accidents occurred in spite of safety precautions; one mishap, just a short while before the mill finally closed, caused the deaths of three men.

TEXTILES

Wool

As in other parts of the country, the textile industry in the Peak District originated in the homes of the people and began with wool. Although much of the wool produced on farms left the district in the raw state, spinning and weaving for family use and for sale was a common domestic activity. A fulling mill, dating back to 1384, is known to have existed at Hartington, and doubtless there were a number of others. But by the eighteenth century, while spinning and the hand-knitting of stockings remained comparatively widespread, the more highly skilled process of weaving had become localised, concentrated—in the national park area—in Yorkshire and the neighbouring districts. The early woollen industry was a vital adjunct to farming. Wool buyers or 'braggers' travelled around buying wool from farmers and supplying it to spinners and weavers; completed work was collected in the same way. Business was profitable for such dealers. Samuel Frith of Combs (Chapel-en-le-Frith) who died in 1828 was one so engaged; he toured the surrounding hamlets with his string of packhorses collecting woollen products from farming people who spun wool and had their own stocking frames; Frith sold the goods in Derby and Nottingham and is said to have built Bank Hall from the proceeds.

The history of the wool trade in the Hayfield district is particularly interesting; a fulling mill, situated near The Ashes on the western slopes of Kinder Scout, operated from early times to the beginning of the nineteenth century. There was much traffic in wool and cloth with strings of packhorses taking material from Hayfield over the Pennines by Woodhead and Holme Moss to Holmfirth for dyeing. Family looms were cherished possessions and often the upper floor of a house or cottage was set aside for weaving work which, in the village of Holme, another closely involved with wool, continued as late as the 1890s; weaving was also done more communally in stone-built sheds, some examples of which, since converted to cottages, can be seen by the roadside at Holme (SE 103056, plate, p 72).

It was the invention and development of machinery for the growing and competing cotton industry which eventually brought mechanisation into woollen manufacture and caused the gradual decline of domestic production. Inventions like Hargreaves's spinning jenny (1764), Arkwright's improved water frame (1775), both combined in and replaced by Crompton's spinning mule (1778) were adapted for wool by the end of the century. Although the spinning jennies could be used in the domestic system, Arkwright's and Crompton's inventions necessitated factory conditions and plentiful water power. Swift streams flowing off the millstone grit, providing power for wheels and suitably soft water for washing processes, invited the siting of woollen mills in remote cloughs in the same way that they influenced general development of the main concentration of the industry in the West Riding, of which such isolated mills formed the fringe.

Thus, at the beginning of the nineteenth century a small number of woollen mills came into existence in the district now covered by the national park. One of these was Gnathole Mill, Charlesworth (SK 039924), built in 1790 by John Robinson on the site of an earlier corn mill and because of its peaty water said to have been renowned for the quality of broad cloths and narrow cloths it produced. Woollen manufacturing was carried on here it seems until about 1880, since when an older building has been adapted for agricultural purposes and the later main mill and offices converted to four flats and a farmhouse. In the centre of this structure is the site of the waterwheel, the power of which was later used for cutting firewood and, more unusually, for churning butter. The water came from Bray and Whitethorn Cloughs and was stored in 'lodges'—a term for millponds used in this area—the remains of which, though partly levelled, can still be seen.

Also remotely situated was Phoside Mill at Hayfield (SK 037859) which was used in the early 1800s for yarn spinning, weaving and cloth dressing. The former mill building is still in existence on the hillside and is now a barn, the waterwheel having been removed in the 1920s. Famed for the size of its waterwheel, Diggle Mill (SE 017080) was one of a number of woollen mills in Saddleworth locality, though most of them situated outside the area of the national park. The wheel was demolished in 1920 but the lodge, wheelpit and part of the original building can still be seen; the premises are now used as a plastics factory.

At Holme, on the threshold of the Holmfirth–Huddersfield woollen complex, the Bilberry fulling mill and two other woollen manufactories stood in the area now covered by the Digley Reservoir. There was also a small woollen mill called Rake Mill (used for spinning yarn for the local weavers) the few remains of which are just discernible beside Rake Dike at SE 105055. Another interesting feature of the woollen industry at Holme, and one easily missed, is a series of twenty-five pairs of holes in stones of a roadside wall on the other side of the village; these extend for some yards from SE 109061, on the east side of the road leading to the Digley Reservoir. Tenterhooks were fixed in these holes for holding the yarn brought here from Rake Mill to dry, and in some the stubs of the wooden pegs still remain (plate, p 72).

Cotton

The cotton industry, like that of wool, existed in the Peak District on a domestic scale before the evolution of the factory system, both processes of spinning and weaving being done in homes.

One area much involved with weaving in the eighteenth century was that of the Hope Valley. The village of Bradwell had a number of small cotton-weaving establishments and many cottages equipped with looms; there was also a manufactory for weavers' shuttles, belonging to the Fox family whose cottage and workshop stood at the bottom of Water Lane. Weaving sheds existed in the village of Hope and some, long since converted to cottages, can still be seen here on the west side of the Edale road at SK 173835; the positions of former doors are easily detectable in the stonework. At Castleton also weaving was done; a reference to an old print of 1743 mentions a mill existing for the purpose on the right of the cavern entrance, by Goosehill. Though the site cannot be definitely identified there are certainly buildings on Goosehill which suggest by appearance that they could have served such a use. Farther south, Stoney Middleton was another place where cotton weaving was carried on in cottages, while at Youlgreave there were formerly weaving sheds beside the River Lathkill at Alport.

Cotton spinning was done fairly generally up to the late eighteenth century on the spinning wheel. By 1776, however, the recently invented spinning jenny, which duplicated the domestic wheel's thread-drawing action, had been introduced at Bakewell and at Youlgreave—localities which had become outposts of the framework knitting industry of Nottinghamshire—and from 1780 to 1800 this piece of equipment, which could be constructed without much difficulty by local craftsmen, was in use alongside remaining spinning wheels throughout the country districts of north-west Derbyshire and in the Staffordshire areas adjoining. In their remoteness from the Lancashire centre of the cotton industry these rural participants concentrated on the production of the coarser yarns and in this field the jenny survived into the nineteenth century.

As well as the spinning done in individual homes, in a number of villages and hamlets small spinning workshops were equipped with several jennies. Evidently Farey's list of places having spinning mills in the nineteenth century includes some of this sort, for at a number of the localities he quotes, including Castleton (said to have had two), Dove Holes and Peak Forest, there appears no record of former actual cotton mills and, though in some places buildings exist which could have served this limited purpose, positive identification is lacking.

The last two decades of the eighteenth century saw the climax of this small-scale cotton industry which was soon being hit by the development of mechanisation and the establishment of mills by Arkwright and others. In the 1760s Richard Arkwright had produced his water-frame roller-spinning machine and in 1771 he built his first mill at Cromford, harnessing the Cromford Sough as his source of water power. This event inaugurated the transition of cotton manufacture from a dispersed, semi-domestic occupation to a more concentrated and mechanised system, and marked the inception of the industrialised era of cotton manufacture. With the abolition of restrictions on the country's use of cotton cloth (imposed previously for protection of woollen manufacture) and the increase of available supplies of raw cotton from the American southern states, the industry in the late eighteenth century was ripe for expansion, and this part of England, in reasonable proximity to Liverpool's importing facilities, with its humid climate and even more important, an abundance of running streams, provided good ground for the establishment of the early factories.

Doubtless it was these factors, together with the accessibility of road communications and the prospects in the small town for labour recruitment, which led Arkwright to Bakewell. In 1777 he negotiated a 50 year lease with Philip Gell of Hopton for land beside the River Wye at Bakewell and within a short time commenced the building of his Lumford Spinning Mill which he presented on completion to Richard, his son. Subsequent events brought difficulties for young Richard Arkwright. Opposition came from the Dukes of Devonshire and Rutland, respective owners of the water rights upstream and downstream of the mill; utilisation of the river to provide water power, involving the changing of its course, had, it was claimed, interfered with the fishing and was allowing only an intermittent supply of water to the Duke of Rutland's ancient corn mill a short distance downstream. Disputes ensued and were not settled until 1786 when Arkwright agreed to pay the Duke of Rutland a nominal rent of £10 a year for a 42 year lease of the water. Following the death of his father in 1792 Richard Arkwright moved from his house at Bakewell to live at Willersley Castle, Cromford, but he retained his ownership of the mill and increased his security by purchasing the freehold from the Gells. In 1821 the running of the mill was taken over by his sons Robert and Peter who before long faced the impending expiry of the Rutland lease. The mill employed about 350 men, women and children (many of them recruited in Manchester) which inflated wage standards, and the succeeding duke, anxious to preserve Bakewell's rural character and to protect agriculture from competition for local labour, was even more resistant than his father. The brothers decided to sell the mill. It was bought by Horace Mason of Calver on a hire-purchase basis, but Mason became insolvent and in 1839 the Arkwrights had the mill on their hands again. After a further unsuccessful attempt to sell in 1840 the premises stood idle for a period, until being leased, with machinery and nearby housing, for cotton spinning in 1844. In 1857 the mill passed to the ownership of the Rev Godfrey Arkwright who in 1860 sold it to the Duke of Devonshire. Subsequently leased, and rebuilt after a serious fire in 1868, the premises continued to function as a cotton mill until the end of the century; in 1898 they were bought by a battery manufacturing firm and run for this purpose until closure by Electric Power Storage Ltd in 1970.

The original mill building, at SK 212691, was long and narrow, the water passing beneath it to operate an undershot waterwheel on the east side. In 1827 this wheel was replaced by a new one of high breast type, larger and more efficient, 25ft in diameter and 18ft wide, with seventy buckets. This, and another smaller one of 21ft diameter

Page 107 (above) *Lamb Hole or Lumb Mill, Kettleshulme, used for many years for candlewick manufacture. The large iron waterwheel inside the building was powered by water from the Todd Brook;* (below) *former mill buildings, now demolished, used originally for silk and later for carpet manufacture, at Wildboarclough. The building in the foreground was Lower Crag Mill, the machinery of which was installed by James Brindley*

Page 108 (above) *Evidence of former terraced cultivation in a field at Bakewell;* (below) *the village pinfold at Hope, used for impounding stray livestock*

and 7ft width, installed in 1852, survived the 1868 fire and were both in use at the factory until a breakdown in 1955, following which they were removed and replaced by a modern turbine. The oldest remaining part of the early mill, dating from at least as early as 1824 and probably from before 1799, is a building which stands adjacent to the river and the A6 road. Upstream are the water reserves, including 'Ashford Lake', the remains of three original mill pools constructed to serve the mill.

Another mill which Arkwright established was at Cressbrook (SK 173726), farther up the Wye Valley in the parish of Litton—a locality already much involved with weaving, framework knitting and other textile skills. Here he leased land recently developed by John Baker, a hosier, who had, amongst other enterprises, started a small distillery for peppermint, lavender and other aromatic herbs which he cultivated. The date of the building of the first mill is uncertain, but it has been estimated by Miss M. H. Mackenzie as 1783, the work of construction having been put in the hands of William Newton, a self-educated poetic joiner from Cockey Farm, Abney. Soon after being built, the three-storeyed building was destroyed by fire on 15 November 1785, but rebuilding took place two years later on the same site. Water power at this stage was provided by the Cressbrook, water from the mill pond passing beneath the road and on to the mill before discharging into the Wye. After Arkwright's death in 1792 the mill, used for cotton weaving, passed into other hands and in 1810 Newton came back as manager. The year 1815 saw the construction of the big mill building of Georgian appearance (plate, p 90) which now dominates the scene; this had two large waterwheels and was powered by the River Wye, dammed to form a mirror-like mill pool in the limestone gorge. Later a steam engine was introduced to supplement the water power in times of drought and in about 1890 water turbines were installed. The mill continued in use for cotton doubling until 1965, but is now used solely for warehousing purposes by a firm manufacturing nylon yarns.

Besides the big mill of 1815 the older one which replaced the

G

original building still stands close by, together with the engineering shop which stands near the river at the end of a long low building on the south side, constructed in 1916. On the north side of the mill buildings there is a row of houses now known as Dale Terrace, but previously called Apprentices Row, where many of the apprentices lived. A portion at the end, of Gothic design, was possibly used as a chapel. Apprentice children at Cressbrook are reputed to have been comparatively well treated; they spent their limited free time at Leisure Farm on the hill above, and walked to Tideswell Church on some Sundays.

Litton Mill (SK 161729), about a mile upstream on the Wye, was opened for cotton spinning in 1782 by Ellis Needham, a notoriously mean character. There were difficulties at the outset, chiefly due to labour problems, and as a solution pauper apprentices were brought from London and other cities to work long hours in the mill and to endure the poor food and harsh and rigorous treatment for which Litton Mill was noted. In 1815 Needham was bankrupt. The mill was subsequently run by others, one being Henry Newton (son of William) and was described in 1857 as an 'extensive spinning and manufacturing establishment' with 400 people employed and using water and steam power. There was a fire at the mill in the 1870s and most of the present buildings are of more recent date, although a building at the bottom of the yard is believed to have been part of an old warehouse, and another, which stands on stone pillars at the higher end, was probably a coach house. An undershot waterwheel of uncertain age is still used for pumping water from a spring on the other side of the river.

In 1934 Litton Mill was bought by the Anglo-French Silk Mills Ltd, and subsequently run as Litton Mills Silk Mills Ltd; artificial silk was produced, and later man-made fibres. A further change of ownership occurred in 1963, and the present firm specialises in the manufacture of textured yarns.

Also founded at the end of the eighteenth century was the cotton mill at Calver, on a site by the River Derwent (SK 247745) which had been previously occupied by a corn mill. It was built by the Gardoms, a family of hosiers, in 1785–6, at the time of expiration of Arkwright's patents, the land being leased from Thomas Eyre of Hassop. The situation, at the junction of turnpikes with a direct route to Manchester, was a particularly favourable one, and with many lead miners and limestone workers in the surrounding area there were plenty of women and children to call on for labour.

The turn of the century was a time of misfortunes for the owners, then trading as Gardom, Pares & Company, for in 1799 a serious flood washed away Calver Bridge and caused havoc at the mill and in 1802 the mill was burnt down. In 1805 it was rebuilt, but because of family deaths and financial difficulties the Gardoms withdrew from the partnership and the management was taken over by a former employee, Horatio Mason, a benevolent and hard-working man who lived with his family at the mill house. About 200 people were employed at the mill in the 1830s, many coming from the neighbouring villages, others living near the mill. Mason was concerned for their welfare; educational facilities were provided for the children and a Sunday school established and conditions were generally less harsh than in many other factories of the time. Sadly, however, due to financial mismanagement, in 1839 Mason found himself bankrupt and running of the mill was taken over by Sir William Heygate, a member of the Calver Mill Company, followed in later years by a succession of others.

Much of the yarn produced at Calver was sent to Leicester for use in the hosiery trade, and cotton spinning continued until the early 1920s when the mill closed down. During World War II the empty building was put into use as a storage depot while the yard became the scene of a crushing and washing plant for fluorspar. After the war the premises were bought by Mr H. G. Sissons, a director of Calver Mill Estate Ltd, and adapted for the manufacture of stainless steel sinks, their present use.

The mill buildings stand on three sides of a square with the main structure—which formerly had six floors and an attic—across the southern end. The yard which the buildings partially enclose was previously the mill pond—the stone-arched spillway is still retained in an adjacent wall—the water being brought along a goit from a weir on the River Derwent at Froggatt New Bridge. In 1833 a new goit was cut, the weir enlarged, and the water made to drive a pair of new waterwheels of 24ft diameter and 17ft width. These were scrapped during the last war but the wheelhouse still stands.

Since establishment of the present firm, previously decaying buildings and their debris-strewn surroundings have been completely transformed. In adapting to the new industry the old mill building has been fully modernised and the unsafe floors replaced by fewer ones, constructed of concrete. Great care has been taken to ensure that additional building blends well with the original work of millstone grit, while the grounds have been landscaped and stocked with a large variety of trees and shrubs. The effect is pleasing, an example of a former industrial site given a new life for modern needs, and enhancing rather than detracting from the surroundings.

Cotton mills which evolved out of former village spinning workshops included those at Bamford and Edale, which, like that at Calver, were both developed on the sites of earlier corn mills. The one at Bamford (SK 205833) was operated from 1782 as a cotton mill by a local farmer and miller, Christopher Kirk, but the earlier building was burnt down in 1791 and it was probably at the time of subsequent rebuilding that power spinning was introduced. The mill was originally powered by the River Derwent but in the nineteenth century a beam engine was installed; it was replaced in 1907 by a horizontal steam engine made by John Musgrave & Sons Ltd of Bolton which continued in use until 1965 and, commendably, is still preserved. Water power, however, is still used for generating electricity by two reaction turbines generating 45hp and 22hp respectively—one of them transferred here from Edale Mill—and until 1951 the mill manufactured its own gas supply. From 1902 the mill belonged to the firm of Fine Spinners & Doublers Ltd and was used for the doubling and reeling of cotton which was brought here from Manchester ready carded and spun; in 1963 the business was taken over by Courtaulds and closed down in October 1965. In 1966 the premises were bought by the Carbolite Company Ltd, and since conversion have been used for the manufacture of electric furnaces and laboratory and research equipment.

The Edale Mill (SK 134854), powered by the River Noe, as well as having been a corn mill had also served as a tannery before being used for cotton. In 1795 Nicholas Cresswell enlarged the premises and took into partnership three Manchester cotton industrialists, James Harrison, Robert Blackwell and Joseph Fletcher, the main, larger mill building with its three storeys and external enclosed staircase probably being added at that time or early in the nineteenth century (plate, p 90). Owned during the nineteenth century by Hector Christie, the mill in its later working days, like the one at Bamford, came under the firm of Fine Spinners & Doublers Ltd. Cotton manufacturing ceased here in 1934 and after subsequent use for storage the mill buildings are at present empty. The old square chimney stack stands nearby. Just west of the mill is the former manager's house, now a private residence, and alongside the road are workers' cottages. Many of the women who worked here, however, lived farther away; a number of them came from Castleton, walking to the mill each day over the saddle in the hills at Hollins Cross, or, in times of bad weather, bringing food with them sufficient for a few days and sleeping meanwhile at the mill.

Another cotton mill established at the end of the eighteenth century was Woodeaves Mill, in Tissington parish (SK 184504). It was built by a hosier, John Cooper, in 1784, and was powered in its early days by water from the Bradbourne Brook, brought along a $\frac{3}{4}$ mile-long mill leat, termed a 'canal', for it was also used for conveying limestone to the mill in small boats. Later, power was provided by a 16hp steam engine. Cotton manufacture, which involved cotton doubling for the lace and curtain trades of Nottingham and elsewhere, continued through the nineteenth century. A hundred people were employed, some of whom lived in cottages in the mill yard and others at nearby

Fenny Bentley. In 1908 production ceased and within a few years the greater part of the buildings were demolished. Left standing were the warehouse and engine house which continued in use for various purposes, including that of a cheese factory. The small portion now remaining is incorporated in a poultry farm while the former manager's house is a private residence, its surroundings transformed though still showing slight evidence of the former buildings.

Established early in the nineteenth century was Clough Mill, Hayfield (SK 032882), one of many which grew up at the time in this district and in the Glossop locality. The mill saw stormy patches, with riots in 1830 and distress at the time of the 'cotton panic' in the 1860s caused by the blockade of American southern ports. The manufacture of cotton ceased in 1920 and since then the buildings have been used for different purposes including poultry keeping, and more recently for the manufacture of paint and of photographic equipment. The main building still remains, but older ones and the tall chimney stack have been demolished.

Besides these comparatively large mills which survived as cotton factories into—or almost into—the twentieth century, there were a number of smaller ones at such places as Brough, Rowarth (New Mills), Rainow and Sheen, where, because of the prohibitive cost of modernisation, general inaccessibility or for other reasons, and due to the gradual drawing-in of the industry to the Lancashire area—more favourable with its coalfields to the advance to steam power—production ceased well before the end of the nineteenth century. In some of these places the buildings concerned have long since vanished, in others there is still something to be seen. Appropriate references and descriptions are included in the Gazetteer.

Flax

From at least as early as the seventeenth century flax grown on farms, particularly on the Staffordshire side of the district, was, like wool, spun and woven in the homes. Wetton is a parish where flax growing, spinning and the weaving of linen were all carried on, and in adjoining Alstonfield a house in the village (SK 129558) was reputedly a centre of flax weaving, though it is not known whether the rear portion of the house was used or if there was a separate building outside. While probably dating from the early eighteenth century, how long this local industry continued is uncertain, though there was at least one linen weaver living at Alstonfield in 1851. The Derbyshire area was probably less involved, though the early industry is believed to have existed at Eyam, its association perpetuated there in the place name Flax Butts.

Flax growing and processing received encouragement during the reign of George III through imposition of duties on foreign linen and the provision of bounties to boost the growth of hemp and flax in this country, and also from the patenting by the flax spinners Edward and James Dakeyne of their water pressure 'disc' engine in 1830. At this time two mills in the district manufactured flax: the Upper Hulme Mill in Leekfrith parish and the one at Gradbach (Quarnford), mentioned in 1834 as being occupied by the flax spinner Daniel de Coin. Both mills were later used for silk.

Silk

With the development of the silk industry at Macclesfield and the building of numerous mills there in the middle eighteenth century, many parts of the Peak District became associated with this branch of textile manufacture, and silk weaving by hand was done in many homes. Hollinsclough and Rainow were villages where such work took place, another was Bradwell where, in 1800, premises at the bottom of Water Lane were in use for the purpose.

At Tideswell, where silk weaving in homes continued until about 1900, there was an agency connected with the Macclesfield trade, supplies of silk yarn being brought regularly to weavers in the area who later returned their finished work. Eyam was a village which co-operated with the Tideswell centre and where silk weaving provided a welcome stop-gap at times when lead mining was at low ebb.

There was specialisation at Eyam in the production of coloured scarves and handkerchiefs for export to Africa, and Ralph Wain, one of three silk weavers there in 1857, evolved a process for reproducing a design on both sides of material. Illiterate and a recluse, he sold his idea to a Macclesfield company by which it was later patented. Wain's factory, now used for shoe manufacture, still stands at the top of the village (SK 213767).

The making of lace from silk and cotton was carried on in the homes of Middleton (by Youlgreave) during the eighteenth and nineteenth centuries: two qualities, very fine and coarse, were produced in black, white and cream for use in the making of parasols, shawls and jackets. Another skilled craft was the covering of buttons with fine silk braid, intricately woven in single strands, by women in the village of Flash (Quarnford) and the surrounding area. An elderly resident of Flash, who inherited the skill from her maternal ancestors, has described the way in which the silk, fetched from Leek (where the finished buttons were also delivered) was worked in exquisite web-like designs, and how the women would sometimes work long hours into the night, earning 1s 3d (6p) a gross, to supplement the wages of their menfolk employed in the Gradbach Mill, in the local collieries or in agriculture.

Besides these small-scale outposts of the silk industry a few actual silk mills were established on the Staffordshire–Cheshire side of the district. The first of these were the Crag Mills at Wildboarclough, whose successful engineering owed much to the millwright ability of James Brindley of later canal fame.

Altogether there were three mills at Wildboarclough, the first of them being Lower Crag Mill (SJ 983686), built in the mid-eighteenth century (plate, p 107). Contractor for the making and installation of machinery was Abraham Bennett, a millwright and wheelwright of Sutton, to whom Brindley was apprenticed. Bennett himself did not give the work due attention and Brindley had to take over. He walked to Manchester on Sunday, his free day, studied carefully the machinery of the Smedley Mill on which the one at Wildboarclough was to be modelled, memorised the details and returned and installed the waterwheel and machinery. The well-designed wheel had a diameter of over 18ft and was of light construction, water being brought from the stream through sluice gates with an ingenious arrangement of crank and pump regulating the supply of water and the speed of the wheel—the whole system a reflection of the illiterate Brindley's natural genius and engineering skill.

The building of the lower mill was followed by construction of the others nearby, at SJ 983687, and the three were later used for other types of manufacture, the main one being the manufacture of carpets. At this time the mills are said to have together employed over 600 people, some of them living in cottages at Wildboarclough, others walking daily from surrounding parishes. One prized production was a large carpet made for the Great Exhibition at the Crystal Palace of 1851.

In the summer of 1958 Lower Crag Mill and, sadly, Brindley's installation, were demolished, as also were the main parts of the larger set of buildings above. Still remaining are the former agent's house and an imposing mill structure, formerly the administrative block, now housing the Wildboarclough Post Office.

Situated also in Cheshire was the Gin Clough Silk Mill at Rainow (SJ 958764), run in the nineteenth century by James Sharpley, a silk throwster, whose supplies of silk were brought from Macclesfield by pannier donkeys. Production ceased apparently in the 1860s after which the premises were adapted for use as a wheelwright's shop. Today the long, low mill buildings, still retaining an old square chimney stack and including a portion nearest the road which formerly comprised a cottage dwelling, are the workshops of a plumbing engineering business. Wood from the old overshot waterwheel has been used for internal doors of the section which forms the present dwelling house, and the area of the mill pond is still apparent.

Near Wincle, but over the Staffordshire border in the parish of Heaton was the Dane Bridge Silk Mill at SJ 963651, now in ruins. This was occupied in the 1860s by Bowden Bower Dakeyn who also ran Gradbach Mill farther upstream at Quarnford (SK 994661). The Gradbach mill was originally built in the eighteenth century or earlier and restored after a fire of 1785. The rectangular two-storeyed building, constructed of millstone grit and, like the mill at Wildboarclough, using cast-iron columns for internal support, has at one end a section which contained the waterwheel. This was very large—of 38ft diameter and equipped with 96 buckets, each holding 35 gal. Such was the arrangement of gearing that one revolution of the wheel is said to have turned the main shaft 2,500 times.

Many of the people who worked in the mill lived in a small industrial village settlement which then existed in the valley. This consisted of many cottages which are now demolished, their traces still remaining in places between the mill and Manor Farm.

Silk production at Gradbach ceased in the early 1870s and the premises were acquired by Sir John Harpur Crewe, and used subsequently as a saw mill and for joinery. They now stand empty, the wheel having been removed some years ago, and the only building now inhabited, in what was once the scene of a busy community, is the former mill owner's dwelling, now a farmhouse.

Farther south, in Leekfrith parish, is Upper Hulme Mill on the River Churnet (SK 012609). This was a silk mill when bought in 1869 by William Tatton of Leek who adapted the premises for silk dyeing, for which the water supply was considered particularly suitable. There was a serious fire here in 1891 and the present premises are mainly modern, though still incorporating some of the earlier structure. The business is still run by the firm of William Tatton & Company Ltd, and now involves processing of synthetic fibres.

One other silk mill in existence in the early nineteenth century was at Alstonfield, where in 1838 sixty-four people were employed. Its exact situation, however, appears unknown.

METAL WORKING

Metal working by the use of water power was formerly carried on at Hathersage for the processes of wire-drawing and the making of needles and pins. The industry is believed to have originated in the village 400 years ago, continuing up to the early years of the present century.

There were four main metal works in Hathersage. The Barnfield Works (SK 229814), formerly that of Messrs Cook, specialised in the production of needles and pins. Massively constructed of millstone grit, the main buildings, together with the old chimney stack, are still standing and, though deteriorated, are used now as a motor repair shop and for joinery. There was also another smaller building just below used for wire drawing and powered by water from the Hood Brook, but this has been demolished and its site is now occupied by a shed. A further, low, building, just beyond the viaduct (SK 228812) was also used in the needle and pin manufacture.

The wire-drawing works of Cocker & Sons, also powered by the Hood Brook, slightly upstream, was on the site of the present Catholic School (SK 229814). It was here that Samuel Fox, who started life making umbrella frames and later started the large steel works at Stocksbridge, Sheffield, served his apprenticeship, riding daily from his home at Bradwell, it is said, on a 'boneshaker' bicycle.

Dale Mill (SK 235817) is believed also to have originally been used for wire-drawing though it has served various subsequent purposes including button-making, engineering, shoe-making and timber, and is now used by joiners and house decorators. The main building is three-storeyed, with a square chimney stack, and on the opposite side of the road are cottages which were formerly connected with the mill.

At the top of Hathersage village, beside the road entering from Sheffield (SK 233816) is another building where wire-drawing was done. The former chimney is demolished and the building is now converted to flats.

LEATHER

The curing of skins, by-products of the district's agriculture, was carried out at a number of tanneries. As already mentioned, the cotton mill at Edale had previously been used for the purpose and a nearby house, known as Skinners Hall (SK 129853) accommodated a number of the workers; they slept in bunk beds in the attic, signs of which still remain. Another tannery was at Bradwell, situated at SK 174812, just behind the old saw mill on the Bradwell Brook; remains of the building still exist though the business ceased at the end of the nineteenth century. The laundry at Grindleford (Eyam Woodlands parish, SK 243773) was also formerly a tannery though the premises have been used for their present purpose since 1913. This must have been a sizeable concern for stone from the demolition of other buildings was used for the construction of a row of cottages which stands here against the road. Another tannery is believed to have existed at the site of the Primrose Vale Mills, Hayfield (SK 032879), later used for making buckram.

The village of Longnor is reputed to have been a centre for saddlery with youths coming from Leek and Buxton to serve apprenticeships. Ruins near Beggar's Bridge on the River Dove (SK 094657) may be remnants of a tannery. Certainly the making of shoes and quarry boots was a thriving trade at Longnor until comparatively recent years, with several small workshops in the village. Shoe-making was in fact a trade found in many places, including Bakewell, which also had a tannery and where, in 1830, there were thirty-seven shoemakers.

At both Eyam and Stoney Middleton shoe-making has attained the status of factory production. At Eyam the industry was apparently introduced by James and John Bromley, and in the latter part of the nineteenth century buildings formerly used for cotton and silk production were adapted for the purpose, some of them since converted to cottages. Various firms were subsequently involved and small subsidiary factories functioned for a time at Bradwell and Hathersage, with many women machining shoe uppers in their homes. The former small silk mill already referred to (SK 213767) is one of two present shoe factories at Eyam, the other being accommodated in a newer building.

Footwear manufacture at Stoney Middleton is believed to have been connected with the Grindleford tannery, the shoes produced being taken to Chesterfield to be sold. There were four or five boot-making concerns in Stoney Middleton, all now having ceased to function except one which occupies the former Carter's Corn Mill (SK 230755) which specialises in the manufacture of footwear of the heavier type. An empty building on the south side of the main road in the village (SK 229755) was used as a shoe factory until the 1960s.

ROPE MAKING

Ropes, so necessary in the past for mining, agriculture and for such purposes as hauling boats on canals, were made at various places in the Peak District, including Bakewell, where there were two rope-walks, Elton, Monyash, Taddington and Upper Hulme (Leekfrith). But perhaps the best-known centre of the trade was at Castleton where, in the unusual situation of the Peak Cavern (SK 148826), the making of ropes has continued on a reduced scale almost up to the present time.

Though unique for the job the cave site had obvious advantages, with ready-made shelter equivalent in size to a large building—the cavern actually contained two cottages in the eighteenth century—and further space for extension of the ropewalk 60yd or more into the cavern's interior if necessary. The cave is reputed to have been used for rope making for over 500 years, and it is said that the Devonshire family gave the ropemakers permission to work in it rent free for as long as there was a ropemaker living, and handing down the trade from father to son or to an apprentice.

The floor of the cavern is roughly divided into a series of longitudinal steps or terraces—eight or nine in all—each terrace having formed a separate ropewalk appropriated by one of the families who plied the trade. The ropemakers operated in pairs, often a father and son on one level with the mother and daughter on another.

Amongst the families associated with the craft here were the Walkers, Dakins, Eyres, Whittinghams and Marrisons, and it is in the hands of a member of the last of these, Mr Herbert Marrison, that the skill has survived in recent times. Mr Marrison was apprenticed here to his father in about 1896 at the age of twelve and spent long hours walking from end to end, twisting the strands of hemp with the aid of 'runner', 'sledge', 'top' and 'cart'—equipment at least 200 years old. With all others here having abandoned the trade and no son to succeed him, and with modern ropes made almost exclusively by machine, it seems that Mr Marrison will be the last of Castleton's long line of ropemakers.

OTHER LOCAL INDUSTRIES

Certain other minor industries have existed at various times of which there are mostly no specific remains, apart from, in some cases, the houses or other buildings where they were carried on.

The making of besoms—brooms made from twigs—was done at Stoney Middleton and also at Thornhill where part of an old building called The Moot (SK 198835) was used for the purpose, though before living memory. Three places concerned with the making of candles, needed not only for domestic use but in large numbers by the lead miners, were Stoney Middleton, Winster (in a building at the top of Woolley's Yard, SK 241605) and Monyash, where buildings in the yard at SK 149664 (opposite the village mere) comprised a small candle factory run by Messrs Harrison, using tallow supplied by local butchers, until early this century.

Hats were made at various places including Baslow and Bradwell. At Bradwell there were about six hatting shops, some on The Hills and some in Smalldale; one kind of hat made here being the 'Bradder beaver', very thick and basin-shaped and worn as a protection by miners (plate, p 18). The last Bradwell hatter was Job Middleton who died in 1899, some years after the manufacture had ceased. The limestone building which he used as his small factory on The Hills is now two cottages—an 'island' encompassed by the minor roadway at SK 176809. His daughters were amongst his staff, he himself travelling the district buying the necessary wool. Hats of a different kind were made at Brook House Clough, Rainow (SJ 947751) where a Mr Neave bought and set up an old mill for the purpose, production continuing until about 1873 when the business moved to Bollington. There are a few remains of the mill incorporated into the present private house and grounds.

Bradwell it seems was a place with a variety of industries, including the making of telescopes, opera glasses and spectacles, which flourished in the village during the nineteenth century, a building at Brookside (SK 174811), formerly a chapel, being one of those used.

The distillery for peppermint and other aromatic herbs operating in the late eighteenth century at Cressbrook (Litton) has already been mentioned (see p 109). The coming into the area of visitors in the nineteenth century prompted the making of mineral waters for their refreshment. One place where this was done was Eyam, where many came to view the scene of the plague, and a factory for manufacturing and bottling was built by Joseph and Walter Wain at SK 216768, though later demolished. A building opposite the school at Castleton (SK 150829), previously a chapel, was also used as a mineral water factory from 1898 to the 1930s, after which it was relegated to a furniture store before becoming empty.

Notes to this chapter are on page 249

CHAPTER FIVE

Water

CONSERVING Peak District water for human needs has been a matter of concern for centuries. But the nature of man's involvement with the problem changed completely during the last century and its sphere of emphasis shifted from the limestone area to the hills and valleys of millstone grit.

In the past, in many of the settlements high on the limestone, clear-flowing water from wells and natural springs was regarded as a very precious commodity, liable so often in the fissured rock to disappear without warning when the watertable became lowered due to dry weather or to the draining of mines. In some places the supplies of water on which people were dependent were treated almost with reverence, as is evidenced in some villages by the continued or revived custom of annual well-dressing ceremonies, when wells are decorated with flowers and other natural substances in religious pictorial designs as thanksgiving for the water—though today supplies in most places come unfailingly through a tap. Many of these old wells are still visible in villages of the area, though in some cases appearances have been altered.

In order to overcome water shortages on the heights rivers were sometimes used, not as supplies in themselves but to provide power for pumping water from springs in the valley to the village above. Such means were employed in the early years of the present century on the River Wye between Litton and Cressbrook Mills for raising water to Cressbrook village; at SK 166729 there are still the partial remains of a small waterwheel, and of the weir, leat and pumping house which were constructed through the generosity of a local benefactress. There was a similar arrangement farther downstream on the south bank of the river (SK 182696), west of Ashford, where a water-

Page 125 (above) *The Sheepwash Bridge at Ashford-in-the-Water, with the holding pen in the foreground. Apertures in the pen's stone walling were for preventing the suffocation of huddling sheep;* (right) *washing sheep in the Bakewell Corn Mill stream, about 1900. In this case the operator did not work standing in the water, as was usual*

Page 126 (above) *The Reapsmoor Cheese Factory, Fawfieldhead, built in the 1870s. The rear extension was added in 1948, but cheesemaking ceased within a few years; (below) reconstructed packhorse bridge in the Goyt Valley, removed from its former site a mile downstream during the making of the Errwood Reservoir in the 1960s*

wheel of approximately 9ft diameter and 5ft breadth is still in position in a small building from which water, piped under gravity from springs near the fishponds, was raised the 500ft to Sheldon village. In the parish of Middleton and Smerrill a waterwheel powered by the River Bradford performed the same function for the inhabitants of Middleton village—only the shell of its building now remains (SK 199633)—and back on the Wye below Buxton there is still in use a turbine-operated pump (SK 093725, Green Fairfield parish) which lifts spring water to Pictor Hall and farms on the hill above.

With the rapid and steady growth of urban populations following the Industrial Revolution, cities and towns on either side of the Peak District started in the nineteenth century to lift their eyes towards its moors, rivers and valleys in their needs for water supplies, and it was to the gritstone areas of high rainfall and water-holding propensity that they looked. Sheffield, in the 1830s, was the first to do so, followed in the next decade by Manchester and in succeeding years by numerous others, in a series of demands which have caused wide tracts of the northern moors to become vast gathering grounds, and which continue in the present day. That such currently functional schemes are mainly far from being 'archaeology' is not denied, yet many have background details worth noting: some by their construction have caused obliteration of former industrial sites, others retain associated features of their actual construction, and a few have been the scenes of disastrous tragedies. Such data has its own deserving place in the area's industrial history.

It was following the formation of the Sheffield Water Company resulting from an Act of Parliament of 1830 that construction of the Redmires Middle Reservoir commenced on Hallam Moors, to be completed in 1836. In 1845 the company obtained a further Act authorising the construction of the Upper and Lower Redmires Reservoirs—impounding all the waters of the Wyoming Brook—and also of the two reservoirs at Rivelin for storing flood waters as a compensation supply for mill owners. The Rivelin Reservoirs were the first of these two schemes to be completed, in 1848, while the

H

Lower Redmires was finished in 1849 and the Upper Redmires in 1854. Designed and constructed by John Towlerton Leather, engineering adviser to the water company, the Redmires Reservoirs, with their banks of centrally clay-puddled earthwork, the noticeable absence of stone or brick masonry and their maximum depth of around 40ft, are typical of the earlier methods of reservoir construction in this country.

In 1852 the company applied for a further Act to authorise diversion of water from Derbyshire's Burbage Brook, but the Bill was defeated due to considerable opposition. In 1853, however, a further Act empowered the company to draw supplies from the two Rivelin Reservoirs on an undertaking that stipulated compensation water was still provided, and in the same year authority was obtained for impounding the waters of the Loxley Valley by the construction of the Dale Dike, Agden and Strines Reservoirs and of the Damflask for compensation supplies.

Construction of the first of these, the Dale Dike, was marked by a major flooding disaster, the greatest of its kind to happen in Great Britain, which occurred around midnight on Friday, 11 March 1864 and caused the loss of 244 lives. The reservoir was still filling when the embankment, constructed obliquely across the valley below the present dam, was damaged on its outer slope by a landslip causing the clay-puddle to subside and the water to overflow. Rapidly the embankment collapsed and an estimated 700 million gallons of suddenly liberated water poured down the valley at the rate of a mile a minute. The havoc was tremendous, and, in addition to the high death roll, the enormous damage to property involved the water company in the payment of £373,000 for injury and loss.

Reconstruction of the Dale Dike Reservoir, with the re-siting of the embankment on more stable ground ¼ mile upstream was authorised by an Act of 1867. Work on this scheme was completed in 1875 but the reservoir was not brought into use until the exceptionally dry year of 1887. Meanwhile construction of others in the group proceeded; the Damflask was constructed in 1867, but a leakage through rocks, discovered as it filled, and the fact that the water was not immediately needed, caused remedial works and the reservoir's use to be postponed for some years. The Agden Reservoir was completed in 1869 and the Strines in 1871.

By an Act of 1887 the water company was taken over by Sheffield Corporation in the following year. In 1897 construction of further reservoirs commenced in the valley of the Little Don: the Langsett Reservoir was completed in 1905 and the Underbank (outside the present national park) in 1907, the Corporations of Rotherham and Doncaster sharing the supply.

A further project of Sheffield's was the damming of the Ewden Valley north of Bradfield in which powers obtained in 1867 were implemented in the construction of the Broomhead and More Hall Reservoirs between 1913 and 1929. Work on these schemes provided welcome jobs for many at a time of unemployment and involved the opening of Rocher Quarry (SK 268954) for supplies of stone, the diversion of the valley road and the construction by the corporation of Ewden village (sited, like the More Hall Reservoir, just outside the park area) equipped with church, recreation room, hospital and canteen, for the workers and their families.

Manchester's ingressions into the area began with an Act of 1846 which authorised the construction of the Woodhead Reservoir to dam the waters of the River Etherow in the Longdendale Valley. Work on this commenced in 1848 and was completed in 1865. Meanwhile work proceeded on others in the chain: the Torside was constructed 1849–69, the Rhodeswood 1849–52, the Vale House 1865–9 and the Bottoms 1869–77, the last two being compensation reservoirs used for the purpose of storing water for discharge daily at a constant rate to maintain the flow downstream. The Arnfield and Hollingworth Reservoirs are two others of this group, constructed during those years, lying just outside the national park. Engineer for the whole of the construction was Mr J. F. Bateman.

Besides the hamlets of Torside, Vale House and Bottoms being submerged, various mills were also affected. At Torside there was a paper mill as well as a bleach works at Crowden. Vale House Reservoir covers the site of the Vale House Cotton Mills—whose chimney remained standing above the water until 1887—and of Rhode Mill, while at Bottoms there was another cotton mill known as Bottoms Lodge Mill. The construction of such huge reservoirs as these—Torside, the largest, covers an area of 160 acres, has a depth of 84ft and a capacity of 1,474 million gallons—have irrevocably changed the whole character of the valley: the mighty water reserves, like the overhead cables of the electric grid and the ever busy lines of communication—road and railway—which also follow this valley, give today an impression of tremendous potential power. From a number of small quarries in the surrounding hillsides stone was extracted during construction of the reservoirs for use in banks and bridges, and the route of a railway track, used during the building of the dams and for maintenance work up to the 1940s, can still be discerned on the reservoir's northern banks, running eastwards as far as Crowden.

Of a number of small supply and compensation reservoirs also now controlled by Manchester Corporation Waterworks in the Glossop locality, some of which lie within the national park and some outside, it is of industrial interest that those at Hurst and Mossylee, built in 1838 and 1840 respectively, are two which owe their existence to a consortium of Glossop mill owners whose aim was to provide an adequate source of water for power and processing. Eventually their ownership passed to the local authority and in 1959 to Manchester Corporation.

Another serious flood disaster of the mid-nineteenth century concerned the earlier Bilberry Reservoir, north-west of the village of Holme, predecessor of one which now forms part of a group controlled by the Huddersfield County Borough Waterworks Department. The original Bilberry Reservoir, of 15–20 acres, was constructed in 1840 at the junction of Marsden Clough and Hey Clough to provide a reserve of water for woollen mills in the valley below. The ealry embankment, measuring 300ft across and about 67ft in height, 16ft thick at the bottom and 8ft at the top, was constructed of earth and stones, with a clay-puddle centre intended to render it water-tight. A bye-wash or waste pit, consisting of a 59ft high circular chimney of about 5yd diameter, sunk through the embankment on the south side and connected to a tunnel which communicated with the water outlet on the lower side of the dam, was designed to allow the discharge of any swiftly rising water with which the normal outlet could not fully cope. This would normally have ensured the water level reaching no higher than 8ft below the top of the dam, but in blasting for foundations for the puddle wall, springs had been broken into which were not properly dealt with and as a result the embank-ment became weakened and leaky, and the level of its centre sunk below that of the bye-wash. Such was the situation in February 1852 when several days of excessive rain on the moorland catchment area coincided with one of the reservoir's shuttles being under repair; work was suspended at the time and the other shuttles blocked, so that only very little water could escape.

The flood burst during the night of 4–5 February and an estimated quantity of 86,240,000gal of water thundered down the valley in an engulfing and terrifying torrent. In thirty minutes the reservoir had emptied and downstream was a sea of destruction. Eighty-one people died and many houses, mills and buildings in the valley to Holmfirth were destroyed or seriously damaged; 7,038 people were thrown out of employment and damage was estimated at £200,000–£250,000. At the inquest which followed it was stated that the reservoir was de-fective in its original construction, the commissioners, engineer and overlooker were all blamed, and the commissioners found guilty of negligence.

Directly below the reservoir embankment stood Broadhead's or Bilberry Mill, a three-storeyed building used chiefly as a fulling mill. Being slightly out of the line of the full force of water, only a part of the building was washed down and its occupants, who had taken refuge there, escaped. Also safe were John Furniss and others who lived at Upper or Middle Digley Mill, 300yd farther on, but the buildings and machinery of Furniss's woollen mill, as well as a large dwelling house and farm buildings were largely swept away. Next down the valley was Digley Mill, consisting of a stone-built mill and large weaving shed of thirty-four looms powered by a steam engine and waterwheel, which with houses, cottages and a farm comprised a small village. These, together with an extensive dyeworks on the left bank of the stream were all demolished, though again the people— unlike others farther downstream who were unprepared and mostly in bed—were saved. Left standing at Digley as a silent reminder for many years was the tall mill chimney stack.

Immediately after the disaster the Holme Valley Commissioners started reconstructing the embankment, this time without the conventional clay core and using a clay envelope 4ft thick laid on the water face of the dam and on the sides and bed of the valley for about 600ft upstream. This still remains today. On the afternoon of 24 May 1944 another storm occurred, about 3½in of rain falling in 2½hr. Fortunately as a safety measure the water level was never allowed to rise above 10ft below overflow level and was 12ft down at the time, nevertheless the reservoir filled rapidly and water rose to within a few inches of the bank top. Had the water spilled over a similar disaster could well have happened, but fortunately this point was not quite reached.

Below the dam, Bilberry Mill was rebuilt, burnt down and rebuilt yet again in the years after the flood, and Middle Digley Mill was reconstructed and resumed function as a woollen mill. From 1915 onwards Huddersfield Corporation had ideas for a further reservoir in the valley and following liquidation in 1936 of the woollen weaving company which owned the rebuilt Digley Mill, an Act was obtained in 1937 for construction of the Digley Reservoir. War caused suspension of the work, the reservoir eventually being completed in 1953. Since its construction no further danger exists from the Bilberry dam, since the water level is the same on both sides.

Less eventful in their construction were the four reservoirs which form a series on Wessenden Moor and which are controlled by Huddersfield Corporation. These are the Wessenden Head, constructed in 1881, Wessenden Old (1890), Blakeley (1903) and Butterley (1906). Another group made for serving Yorkshire woollen districts and now collectively administered by the Mid Calder Water Board also lies in the north-eastern sector of the national park; the first of them to be constructed was the Dunford Bridge Reservoir (1858), followed by Lower Windleden (1872), Yateholme and Riding Wood (both in 1874), Ramsden (1881), Upper Windleden (1890), Harden and Snailsden (both in 1899) and Brownhill—part of which lies within the park—in 1924. All the dams are of earthwork construction. The ancient Yateholme farmhouse, which stood in the catchment area and was demolished in the post-war years, has been partially preserved; its front façade and porch were re-erected in a park at Holmfirth and the back porch behind the Fleece Inn in the village of Holme.

Valleys in the north-western extremity contain reservoirs which supply the Saddleworth area. These consist of Yeoman Hay (1880), Greenfield (1903), Chew (1912) and Dove Stone (1967). All are of conventional earthwork construction and are controlled by the West Pennine Water Board.

Farther south the needs of Stockport caused the construction of the Kinder Reservoir, completed in 1912; this was originally intended to have a masonry dam, but plans were changed and an earthwork embankment substituted. Continued demands by Stockport led to the construction of the Fernilee Reservoir in 1937 involving flooding of part of the Goyt Valley, when the ruins of the old gunpowder mill (see p 100) were submerged below the reservoir's 1,087 million gallons. More recently the Stockport and District Water Board have built a second reservoir immediately upstream—the Errwood, of 927 million gallons capacity, completed in 1967. Construction of the Errwood Reservoir necessitated some alterations to communications in the valley and the diversion of the road known as The Street; a bridge was built over an arm of the reservoir, a new road made of part of the Cromford & High Peak Railway's route and the packhorse bridge which formerly crossed the Wildmoorstone Brook near Goyts Bridge was removed and reconstructed a mile upstream (plate, p 126).

Macclesfield & District Water Board has two reservoirs in the national park area: Trentabank, which straddles the western boundary, was completed in 1929 and Lamaload, near Rainow, in 1962. A stone shield bearing the inscription 'E.J. 1739' was removed from above the front door of Trentabank Farm when the house was demolished and has been incorporated in the concrete approach to the pier reaching out to the reservoir valve tower. South yet again is another of the park's newer water schemes, the Staffordshire Potteries Water Board's Tittesworth Reservoir which at its northern end lies within the area in Leekfrith parish. Construction was completed in 1962 and incorporated an older and smaller reservoir—outside the park—built in 1848. The former corn mill at Meerbrook came within the area of the enlargement and was demolished prior to flooding.

Perhaps the most spectacular scheme is that which involved the flooding of the upper Derwent and Ashop Valleys and the drowning of their respective villages by the making of the Howden, Derwent and Ladybower dams. At the end of the nineteenth century these deep-sided dales were tempting ground for prospecting water engineers, and the Corporations of Derby, Leicester and Sheffield all sought powers to impound the water for their respective needs. As a result the Derwent Valley Water Board was formed and an agreement reached for supplying water to Derby, Leicester, Nottingham and Sheffield Corporations and to Derbyshire local authorities; the Board was incorporated under an Act of 1899 and construction of the reservoirs in a series of instalments was empowered.

Work on the Howden dam began in 1901 and on the Derwent dam in the following year. Of similar design they are both constructed of masonry, 178ft thick at the base tapering to 10ft at the top; the Howden dam is 117ft high and 1,080ft long and the Derwent 114ft high, 1,110ft in length. As already described in Chapter Three, stone for the dams' construction was obtained from the Bole Hill Quarries near Hathersage; it was brought by rail from Grindleford station to sidings at Bamford whence transport continued along a standard-gauge line—its route still partially traceable—northwards up the western side of the Derwent Valley to Birchenlee. Here, on land now afforested, a temporary village of huts was constructed by the board for the workmen and their families—around 1,000 people in all—with a school, mission hall, hospital, recreation room and shops. The Howden Reservoir, of 1,980 million gallons capacity, was in use in 1912 and the Derwent Reservoir, holding 2,120 million gallons, in 1916.

In order to increase the available supply, powers were obtained in 1920 for diversion of water from the Rivers Ashop and Alport to the Derwent Reservoir, and this work, which involved weirs across the rivers and an aqueduct with a tunnel through the intervening hills, was completed in 1930.

Construction of the Ladybower dam commenced in 1935 and continued under difficulties during the war years; filling of the reservoir commenced in 1943 and the works were formerly inaugurated by King George VI on 25 September 1945. For geological and other reasons the Ladybower dam is of different construction from the other two in the Derwent Valley; 1,250ft long and 140ft high, tapering in thickness from 665ft to 17ft, the embankment is of earthwork with a clay core, with deep trenches and boreholes in the ground below packed with concrete to prevent seepage through the underlying strata. Water surplus to the reservoir's capacity of 6,300 million gallons escapes through two funnel-shaped overflows. Clay for the embankment came from land between Bamford and Hope while necessary stone was obtained from adjacent quarries and also from Birchover. The Ladybower scheme, which caused the submergence of the villages of Derwent and Ashopton, also necessitated the reconstruction of the intersecting roads through the valley and the building of two large viaducts.

As demands still increased, powers were obtained between 1944 and 1956 for taking water from the River Noe, the Peakshole Water and the Bradwell Brook to augment the reserves. Consequently water from the Noe is now conveyed through the hills from Edale to the Ashop Valley, and that abstracted from the Peakshole Water at

Castleton and from the Bradwell Brook near Bradwell is carried by a tunnel through Win Hill into the Ladybower Reservoir—schemes completed in 1951 and 1960 respectively.

The North Derbyshire Water Board, formed by the amalgamation of numerous local authorities in 1962, in addition to receiving supplies from the Derwent Valley, has under its control several small reservoirs in the northern part of the county. Of these, Ramsley and Barbrook are within the national park, situated on the moors between Baslow and Holmesfield; both have clay-cored earth embankments and were constructed in 1901 and 1908 respectively.

Notes to this chapter are on page 250

CHAPTER SIX

Agriculture

STILL today a leading industry of the Peak District, agriculture has for many centuries been one of its chief forms of livelihood. In the past, as now, there were limitations due to altitude and climate to contend with, and problems, too, concerning soil fertility and water conservation and disposal, less formidable to modern farmers but in earlier days calling for considerable toil and resourcefulness. Over the years there have been many changes, not only in methods but in the systems of land use, in the kinds of crops grown and the types of stock kept. Though the picture of man's early agricultural activities is far from being clear or complete, relics do exist to give some indication of the district's bygone agricultural practices, while the present landscape owes much of its composition to the farming developments of the last two centuries.

EARLY FARMING

Although grassland now predominates there is considerable evidence of former arable farming in the Peak District, particularly in the limestone area. In certain places it is possible to see in the fields lines of undulations, generally parallel, known as lynchets, which are regarded as signs of earlier cultivation. Some of them, like those which appear west of the A515 road at Tissington (SK 166517), are very pronounced; others are less easily discernible and clearly seen only when the grass is short and the sun low in the sky.

A rare example of a pre-Saxon farming system described, for want of a better term, as 'Celtic fields', exists on sloping land south of the River Wye near Miller's Dale in Blackwell parish at SK 131731.

Surveyed in 1969 by Mr F. Thomas, lines of the fields, of fairly regular shape, partially obliterated by later lynchets and super-imposed by stone walls, cover an area of about 25 acres. They are visible under suitable conditions from the Miller's Dale–Wormhill road on the opposite side of the valley.

Considered to be of somewhat later date and attributable possibly to the Anglo-Saxons who penetrated the area from the south-east by way of the river valleys, are examples of former terraced cultivation. One such site, at Priestcliffe, near Taddington (SK 142717), consists of thirteen large step-like terraces running approximately north and south on sloping ground, at an altitude of around 1,100ft; it was investigated in 1958 by a party of members of the Buxton Archae-ological Society under Dr J. Wilfrid Jackson. Another good example can be seen immediately west of the town of Bakewell, north of the road to Monyash at SK 213684 (plate, p 108).

While the gritstone area, prior to denudation by lead smelters, was still largely wooded and mainly uncultivated, it seems likely that by the Middle Ages the open field system of agriculture was fairly com-mon practice in villages on the limestone, even up to about the 1,300ft level, as well as in the valleys. There is evidence that a good deal of land came under cultivation subsequent to the Domesday survey, with the majority of villages having their open fields of individual strips for corn growing. Often it is possible to identify the locations of such strips from surviving lines of 'ridge and furrow', and a study by Dr W. E. Wightman gives evidence that these existed fairly widely. Although his list enumerates sites which relate chiefly to existing settlements, a few were associated with villages that are now dis-inhabited and vanished—except perhaps for a farm—and surviving only in a parish name. Cold Eaton (near Alsop), Gratton and Harthill are such examples, and two others, Nether Haddon and Edensor, were villages purposely destroyed or removed to make way for the respective sitings of Haddon Hall and Chatsworth; all of them showing signs of former open field cultivation.

Usually the arable land lay fairly close to the village nucleus and consisted of one, two or three fields divided into elongated strips, each strip being apportioned to a different individual. Naturally the areas of better soil and greater physical advantage were selected for preference. The up-and-down method of ploughing, and the type of plough used, threw the soil to the centre line of each strip causing the characteristic ridges, while the alternating lines of depression resulted from either a double furrow or a headland of unploughed land which divided one strip from the next. A group of strips in alignment was called a furlong and either this or the whole field probably constituted a unit in a two- or three-course rotation of crops. Apparently due to the type of plough used and its need for turning space is the gentle S-shaped curve which the lines of ridge and furrow sometimes display. Though it may be difficult to discern this from ground undulations alone, the curve is sometimes quite obvious from stone walls which may follow the lines, one example being seen east of Castleton village, easily observable from the Pindale–Castleton road. Often it is quite possible to identify a parish's former area of open field cultivation by blocks of small narrow fields which exist close to many of the villages, as, for example, south-east of Longnor. Sometimes they are adjoined by other similar fields running at right angles, forming a definite pattern on the larger-scale ordnance survey maps. The walls of such fields generally differ from those of later enclosure by being lower and of less specific construction.

Not to be confused with the open field system, however, is the series of long, parallel, walled fields which stretch out on either side of the village street at Chelmorton. With water being a particularly valued commodity in this parish—situated on the limestone on the 1,100ft contour—settlement was governed by the route of a stream, now piped, which followed the line of the present road, and crofts became closely established on either side of it, each one enclosing a length of land out of the waste. Chelmorton, nevertheless, was not without an acreage of open field arable land; documentary evidence relating to the later Enclosure Acts proves its existence, though visible signs have disappeared.

When arable strips were walled is not precisely known, but this early enclosure probably proceeded gradually during later medieval times, no doubt as the greater interest shifted towards livestock. There had been a general decline in arable cultivation since the Black Death which reached Derbyshire in 1349 and caused depopulation of villages, shortages of labour and a lasting increase in wages. It seems likely that the enclosure of strips was done chiefly for the purposes of stock farming—probably due to their falling out of cultivation for want of hands to work them—otherwise turning the plough in such a confined walled area would prove difficult for efficient land use. The advantages for stock would make the walling a worth-while project: segregation and management of the animals would be easier, disease could be better controlled and bellanding (poisoning due to grazing lead-bearing pastures)—a persistent trouble with the increased spread of the mines—could be avoided.

Another important influence in the swing to stock farming was the establishment of numerous monastic farms, outposts of abbeys, known as granges. Though probably having some arable land the granges concentrated mainly on sheep, contributing to the considerable increase in the sheep population during the Middle Ages stimulated by the demands of the country's thriving wool trade. The names of most of these granges survive today in present farmhouses distributed fairly widely over the national park; an example is Wincle Grange, originally built in about 1380 by Cistercians from northern France as an outlying farm of the abbey at Combermere. It is believed that, until the Reformation, Wincle Grange was a collecting point for wool produced in the surrounding area and sent over to the Continent for use by Flemish weavers. Once the granges had led the way and demonstrated the advantages of well-organised stock farming other farmers followed. Restrictions of the old medieval system began to crumble and agriculture started slowly to expand.

In conjunction with the open field system small reserves of meadow were set aside as grass for hay, while stock were pastured in permitted numbers on the areas of unenclosed common land. Pasture land was commonly let as 'gaits', a system of ancient origin which still continues in some areas. Thorpe is one parish where it was practised; a gait, equivalent to approximately 2 acres, was rated as the grazing of 1 cow, or of 2 young oxen, 4 sheep, 3 sheep with followers, or 3 geese, and anyone could rent gaits on Thorpe Cloud or Thorpe Pasture as they became available. But from the fourteenth century onwards, as the numbers of cattle and sheep multiplied and the advantages of enclosure became obvious, increasing amounts of pasture or waste land were taken in and enclosed as 'intakes', often involving the creation of new farms. For some time this process went on fairly freely but gradually it became apparent to commoners that they were losing good grazing ground and by the end of the fifteenth century there were disputes. One such affair occurred at Over Haddon where the Abbot of Leicester had enclosed common land in Lathkill Dale. A suit was brought against the abbot and in 1530 inhabitants of Over Haddon broke down some of the enclosure hedges and let in their stock, but in the ensuing trial the abbot's case was upheld.

A relic of these early agricultural systems of livestock management which can still be found in many places is the village pinfold, a small walled enclosure, round, rectangular or irregular in shape, in which stray cattle or sheep were impounded. The man who kept charge of the pinfold was called the pinner or pinder, and it was his legal obligation to feed and water the animals, and to notify the owner and receive from him the money necessary for their return. This amounted to a levy of a certain sum per head payable as compensation for crops eaten or damaged, plus a smaller amount for each due to the pinner for the cost of food. If the owner refused to pay, the cost of the animals' keep while impounded could be recovered by selling them one at a time. Almost every village in this part of the country possessed a pinfold and although many are now forgotten and a large number completely or partially removed, there are some good examples still in existence. The best preserved is a circular one at Hope, situated by the bridge over the Peakshole Water, beside the Pindale road, at SK 172833 (plate, p 108). It has a diameter of about

15ft and limestone walls about 6ft in height with a bolted wooden door, and is still used on occasions. As recently as 1967 a total of 300 sheep over the year were impounded in the Hope pinfold, charge for their recovery being 2s 6d (12½p) a head in summer, and 1s 6d (7½p) in winter (the charge higher in summer because of the greater potential damage to growing grass and crops) in addition to 2d (1p) per animal for the pinner. Expenses of transport—or in modern times of telephoning—involved in informing the owner can also be claimed by the pinner at Hope who is obliged to convey the information personally, and not by letter, as a guarantee that word is received. The owner risks a fine of £500 if he illegally breaks into the pinfold to retrieve his stock.

Another pinfold—square in shape—still preserved though disused since 1921, is at Hathersage, situated beside Church Bank at SK 234818. Also square, walled with millstone grit and comparatively large in size, is the one at Bradfield, which lies beside the Sheffield road at SK 269923; let at a nominal rent as a garden it is still used unofficially at times for securing stray animals. Biggin, in Hartington Nether Quarter, and Waterfall, near Waterhouses (SK 155593 and SK 082513), both retain circular pinfolds more recently filled with refuse or ashes. References to a number of others are made in the Gazetteer.

Features of even earlier origin to be found near some villages and hamlets are ancient ponds or meres, used for centuries by farmers to counter water shortages in the dry upland parishes. These meres, some of which cover nearly an acre in area, were apparently made by deepening the rocky ground over the site of a natural spring. Farey lists a number of them, of which a particularly good example today is the one at Monyash, situated beside the road leading southwards from the village (SK 150664).

Page 143 (above) *Coldwall Bridge across the Dove near Thorpe. The bridge carried an early coach road across the river, but is now virtually disused;* (below) *northern portal of the Newhaven Tunnel on the Cromford & High Peak Railway. The plaque on this side bears the railway's crest and the names of the engineer and clerk*

Page 144   (above) *Western portals of the Woodhead Tunnel, photographed 1967. The middle tunnel was the earliest, the one on the left now carries the electric power line, while the modern right-hand tunnel takes the present electrified railway;* (below) *the double viaduct which carried the Midland railway across the River Wye and the road at Miller's Dale. The curved, nearer structure is the older, constructed when the line was built, in the early 1860s*

LATER DEVELOPMENTS

By the middle of the eighteenth century there was a general feeling of restlessness amongst some of the farmers of the Peak District. In spite of the series of earlier enclosures by agreement with landowners, a large proportion of the land remained unenclosed, some still as open field arable but the majority as moorland waste and common grazing of poor and unmanaged grassland. By this time forward-looking farmers, conscious of the agricultural advances of the day, were aware of the benefits achieved by enclosure, of the increased possibilities for modernisation and higher productivity, and of the financial advantages to be gained. Already the movement for Parliamentary Enclosure was under way in other parts of England and many Peak District agriculturalists, particularly in the limestone area of northwest Derbyshire, were impatient to participate. As might be expected, there was opposition to the idea, particularly, with some justification, from the small freeholder. But as soon as there was a group of promoters in favour representing not less than a third of the total interest a scheme for enclosure could be drawn up and Parliament petitioned for the introduction of a Bill. Once the Act was passed, commissioners named in the bill extinguished the common rights and arranged the redistribution of the land. Those receiving allotments were responsible for the cost of their walling and also for a share of the expenses of promotion, and if they failed to pay their land could be sold or let by the commissioners to cover the cost.

Consequently, in the years between 1760 and 1830 vast acreages of the area were enclosed, many new farms were made, roads constructed, and long regular walls built in geometric pattern over the countryside. Walls built under the enclosure acts had to comply with specified standards of height, width and slope, and have a stipulated number of 'through' stones in their construction, as laid down by the commissioners. Appearing as they did quite rapidly following the

I

granting of the awards for a particular parish, these walls caused pronounced changes in the landscape within a very short time. One may wonder if any objecting voices were raised concerning their aesthetic effects such as would undoubtedly be heard today.

The creation of new farming units added many farmhouses to the scene at the end of the eighteenth and early in the nineteenth century. Peak District farmhouses, including the older granges and 'halls'— many rebuilt or extended at this time or earlier—are mainly well proportioned and almost invariably constructed of either limestone or millstone grit. Common items of domestic equipment included gritstone water troughs (often used out on the farm too, for horses and cattle drinking), massive cheese presses comprising deep rectangular stone blocks, and substantial stone bread ovens, while some farmhouses had a special structure of brick or stone supporting a large bakestone over a fire for the regular cooking of oatcakes. Such relics are only rarely found today, though in some places a trough or stone cheese press reposes in a farm yard or garden.

Besides having buildings for housing cows and for other purposes adjoining their dwellings, many farmers at this time also built stirk houses on their outlying pastures. These stone structures, usually quite small and with an overhead loft, were used for storing hay and for providing shelter for young stock in winter. A number of stirk houses are still used in this way, but some, due to changed methods of farming and the tendency to winter animals closer to the farmstead, have become superfluous and fallen into disrepair. It was also common practice to construct a stone sheep pen in the corner of a field so that sheep could be easily caught and held for sheep shearing and feet paring, while another kind of aid to stock management was a small space arranged in the construction of some walls to serve as a sheep creep, big enough to allow sheep but not cattle to pass through. A large flat stone enabled the gap to be closed when necessary. Such simple devices can obviously still be of use in places and there are numerous fields where examples can be seen.

A feature of many farms in the limestone area, and particularly

numerous around Over Haddon and Monyash, are meres (often in-
correctly termed 'dew-ponds') constructed by farmers to provide
water for stock to drink. These differ from the ancient ponds or meres
already described (p 142) in being smaller, more regularly round in
shape, and fed by surface water rather than by natural springs. Farey,
writing in 1815, describes the method of construction practised at the
time in Hartington. A circular hollow, 10–20yd in diameter, was dug
on a hill slope and the soil, rubble and rocks laid in a wide and
regular bank around the edge. The sides were made to slope regularly
towards the middle where the depth would be 3–3½ft. In the hollow a
5in layer of limekiln ashes was first spread, well trodden down by men
or beaten with wooden hammers. Next a 4in covering of well-
tempered water clay was thickly laid and well rammed down, followed
by a second bed of the same thickness. Then, before the clay solidified,
the bottom and edges were paved with rubble stones and this covered
by a last layer of smaller rubble and gravel, several inches thick.
Finally a furrow was ploughed in the grass field to direct water from
the higher ground into the pool. Meres are frequently seen sited near
the roadside wall of a field enabling water intake by a run-off channel
from the edge of the road. In recent years a number of field meres
have been lined with cement; however, due to the general un-
desirability and the health hazards of this stagnant water for animal
drinking, many have now been fenced off or encircled by protective
walls to prevent access, the water in some cases still being used, but,
more hygienically, piped to a trough.

CROPS

It seems likely that crops under the open field system consisted
mainly of rye and oats, with wheat and barley less commonly grown,
as well as beans and other legumes. Units were probably cropped
under a three-course rotation, possibly of beans followed by a corn
crop, with the ground left fallow in the third year to rest it and

control weeds. Fertility of the soil was aided by grazing of the stubble by stock, generally an essential part of the system.

Arable farming was still commonly practised and even increasing in the limestone area of Derbyshire in the mid-nineteenth century, when a fifth of the enclosed land was under cultivation; a climax was reached in 1870 after which there was a steady decline. In general the limited cropping of wheat was mostly confined to the lower areas; Farey records seeing it grown in north Derbyshire at Bakewell, Blackwell, Chisworth, Hope, Over Haddon and Stanton-in-the-Peak. Barley he noted at Youlgreave and Over Haddon, presumably for supplying a brewery at Baslow. The flail was still in use for threshing in the early nineteenth century, though mechanical means in the form of a horse-powered thresher working on the gin principle, and the threshing-box driven by a steam engine were coming into use. The Staffordshire hill country, though predominantly grass-growing, also saw some intensification of arable from 1775, chiefly in the growing of oats and root crops, and also of flax. Many portions of moorland waste became smallholdings at this time, with 'squatters' enclosing for themselves acreages of peat and heather, improving fertility by burning the peat and mixing it with lime—known as 'ess'—and cropping with oats and potatoes. Oats, the cereal most suitable for cultivation at the higher altitudes, was important for providing the meal for oat bread, porridge and oat-cakes—mainstays of the diet, particularly in the poorer homes.

Maintaining fertility was always a problem, not only on the acid moorland soils but also on the limestone from which nutrients rapidly drain. The use of lime and the very frequent occurrence of limekilns on farms has already been discussed in Chapter Three. Potash was made available by the burning of turf and ling when rough land was reclaimed, and phosphates were added by the application of ground bones produced by various mills (see Chapter Four). The need for nitrogen, met partly by the growing of leguminous crops but supplied chiefly from animal manure, emphasised the Peak District farmer's dependence on livestock husbandry.

LIVESTOCK

Up to this point the millstone grit uplands have barely been considered in the district's agricultural history. Only their intervening valleys supported any attempts at cultivation, with the wet moorlands and the previously afforested land—divested of its trees by the lead miners—remaining largely as waste. But sheep farming has a long tradition in this extensive hill country, and with much land on the lower slopes coming under enclosure in the nineteenth century the rearing of cattle became a feature also.

Implementation of the Enclosure Acts produced marked effects upon the Peak District's livestock population. A minor point of interest is that geese, formerly commonly kept by cottagers (land by the River Bradford at Middleton, called Gooseholme, is said to have been one place used for their grazing) went sharply into decline. Of greater import was the continued increase in the sheep numbers, at least for the time being, and the sharp rise in those of cattle.

The oldest native breed of sheep still to be found in the district, though now in very reduced numbers, is the Woodland White-faced, which took its name from the formerly wooded upland area of Hope Woodlands. Farey records the breed as being in his day the most numerous in the mountainous regions of Derbyshire and in the neighbouring parts of Yorkshire and Cheshire, with about eighty farmers keeping the breed. Characterised by their white faces, the Woodland sheep have white, rather long legs, and both rams and ewes are horned; they were previously kept for their wool which was improved by crossing with Merino rams introduced early in the nineteenth century. Good-sized flocks of the Woodland White-faced sheep were maintained up to World War I after which there was a decline, until in 1939 the breed was almost extinct. It is kept alive today only by two or three principal breeders.

Commonest on the high limestone of Derbyshire and adjoining

Staffordshire, prior to enclosure, were sheep of the Old Limestone breed; large, heavy and bony, without horns and with thick skin and coarse wool. It was probably early crossing of this breed with the Woodland White-faced which produced the Dale-of-Goyt or Derbyshire Gritstone; the Gritstone, a hardy breed, devoid of horns and with a speckled face and legs, was first shown at Bakewell Show in 1906 and is now a predominant breed within the national park.

A summer job for farmers and shepherds in the past was the washing of sheep before shearing. This was usually done in a particular part of a river or stream where there was a natural pool of suitable depth, with easy access from the banks. In some cases the water would be partly dammed by a wall of stones, and often pens were constructed on the banks beside the sheepwash for holding the sheep prior to washing. Early June was usually the time for this, and sheep would be brought down from the hills to the customary place to be immersed and their wool cleansed of grit and dirt. One of the men had to stand in the deep water to handle each sheep in turn, drawing apart the wool for the water to penetrate; a cold job and one which demanded the provision of warming spirits for the operator. For the sake of physical well-being it was important that the drink was taken after and not before being in the water though sometimes this rule was disregarded with unfortunate effects; not only drunken incapability—hazardous in the deep water—but severe hypothermia might result.

Almost every village had its special sheepwash and some had two or more; in Over Haddon parish there were four. The best-known example is the one below the sheepwash bridge at Ashford-in-the-Water (SK 194696, plate, p 125). Here, before going into the river, the sheep were held on the south bank of the Wye in a stone pen with apertures in its walls to prevent suffocation of huddling sheep. They entered the water directly from it and after washing were led away downstream and around the outside of the pen. Due to its convenient situation and layout the Ashford sheepwash was used for washing sheep not only from nearby Ashford and Sheldon but also from parishes as far off as Flagg and Monyash, often not without some confusion and mixing of sheep. This particular one is owned by the parish council to which a payment of 6d a score or part score of sheep washed was—and still is—officially due. In a number of places there are pens or other stonework remaining from a former sheepwash, and a number of such sites are described in the Gazetteer.

As in most other parts of the country, the practice of washing sheep seems now to have died out. Onecote is one of the last parishes where it was done, just a few years ago. It became apparent that the extra sum paid for washed wool did not cover the combined cost of the wool's loss of weight, the labour involved, the occasional sheep casualty and the bottle of whisky necessary to keep the operator warm.

The breeding of cattle, as of sheep, has been one of the Peak District's chief farming pursuits at least since the time of Domesday; Bakewell and Monyash are two townships which received grants of markets or fairs during the thirteenth or fourteenth centuries. Gradually intensified during medieval times and markedly increased following parliamentary enclosure, cattle became of greater importance as the need for dairy produce rose with the growth of industry and urban populations.

Up to the year 1800 oxen were commonly employed for draught purposes—even in the early nineteenth century Farey recorded some still being used. The Duke of Devonshire usually had a team of 8 oxen at work on his farm at Chatsworth, worked 4 at a time on alternate days, and 4 teams of spayed heifers were kept in regular work at Great Hucklow. Working oxen were generally later sent to more lush pastures for fattening, as were young stock reared for beef on the hills. At the end of the eighteenth century Staffordshire was one of the main sources of store animals for the Midlands, the most general breed at the time still being the ancient Longhorn, a heavy, long, low-bodied beast, dark red brindle in colour with a white stripe along its back and white spots on the thighs, which eventually died out. The High Peak was also the home of the Blue Albion, a blue-roan beast which retained its popularity up to the 1920s and thirties but which is now virtually extinct. In type the Albion was similar to the Shorthorn which, with other breeds, gradually became predominant.

DAIRYING

The making of butter and cheese for home consumption and for sale, as an adjunct to stock farming, was carried on for many years in farmhouses of the Peak District. Some of these, particularly on the Derbyshire–Staffordshire border, still retain old cheese presses and other equipment used for their manufacture, and elderly members of farming families recall cellars or upper-floor rooms used for ripening and storage. In the early 1800s grass on most farms was ill-managed and in a very poor state; the best land at Tideswell, for example, let at 16s (80p) an acre, would summer only 1 cow to 3 acres producing 4cwt of cheese—the equivalent of 150gal of milk per acre. But as the nineteenth century progressed and stocking rates increased milk became more plentiful, milk which, in the absence of satisfactory transport, could only be suitably marketed in the form of long-keeping quality cheese. Prices paid in the towns for cheese, however, were often hopelessly low and it was not unknown for farmers to cart Derby cheeses all the way to Derby Cheese Fair and to bring them back again for this reason.

A means for disposal of milk was provided by a number of small cheese factories set up towards the end of the nineteenth century, quickly following the establishment of England's first purpose-built cheese factory at Longford near Derby in 1870. These were mainly built through the interest of the lord of the manor or some prominent landowner, and run by farmers on a co-operative basis, managed by a committee. Money for financing the system was subscribed by the farmers who supplied the milk, at the rate of £1 or less per milking cow. The amounts so raised were not great, but brought in sufficient for running expenses, since farmers were not paid for their milk until the cheese was sold. Payments were made on account as and when the cheeses were marketed, with a final settling in the new year when all the cheeses had been disposed of and paid for.

With the bulk of milk being produced in the summer, the factories operated on a 6–8 months basis, from spring to autumn. Most cows were dry during winter, except perhaps for one kept for the household, when surplus milk would be made into butter. During the season cheesemaking was a seven-day-a-week job and involved long hours for the factory managers who were often assisted by their wives. The managers, whose salaries varied from £100–£150 per year, were themselves responsible for financing any extra labour required, and, if paid at the higher rate, also the cost of coal, rennet, salt and cloths necessary for the cheesemaking. One of the leading pioneers was Mr William Gilman who had several of the factories under his care; in the early 1870s he visited Russia to teach the making of Derby cheese, a service which earned him grateful appreciation.

Derby cheeses were the type made originally, but at some factories other varieties were later introduced. The Hartington factory was started on land near the River Dove (SK 126604) soon after 1870, with an initial daily intake of 50gal of milk. Pigs were kept as a sideline for consumption of the whey. In the 1890s, however, with cheesemaking subject to competition from increasing liquid milk sales, a decline set in. The Hartington factory became very dilapidated and from 1894 to 1900 stood unused and derelict. Then it was taken over by Mr J. M. Nuttall, a Stilton cheesemaker from Leicestershire whose business had suffered due to foot-and-mouth disease. One of three founders of the British Dairy Farmers' Association, he adapted the Hartington factory and brought in the manufacture of Stiltons. The new business, welcomed by farmers in the locality, was formed into a private company in 1916, the year before Nuttall died. A fire in 1929 which destroyed the old structure of wood and corrugated iron caused only a temporary lapse in cheesemaking, which was soon resumed in a more suitable new building constructed on the site. In 1962, after being run for some years by the Brindley family, the firm of J. M. Nuttall & Company was taken over by the Milk Marketing Board. Production of Stiltons still continues at the Hartington cheese factory—the only one still functioning in the Peak District—both for the home market and for export.

Also founded in the early 1870s was the Reapsmoor cheese factory

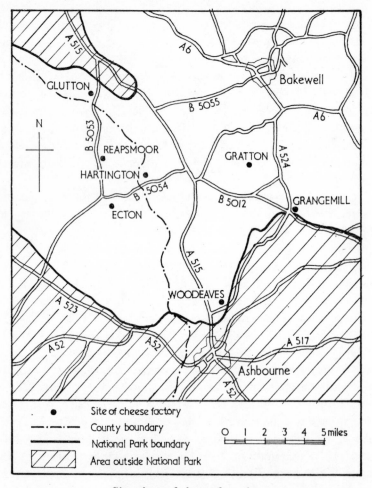

Situations of cheese factories

(Fawfieldhead parish, SK 087619). This was built on land given by Mr William Shirley with materials provided by Miss Prince, of The Brund, Sheen, whose nephew and heir, Professor John Prince Sheldon, was a noted authority on agriculture and dairying. Farmers who could afford bought £5 shares, others contributed their labour for the building. Originally called the Hulmes Dairy, the co-operative concern later became the Manifold Valley Dairy Association. On 1 October 1935 the Co-operative Wholesale Society took over for one year and on 1 October 1936 the business was sold to Express Dairies Ltd, when Cheddars, Cheshires and Caerphillys were subsequently made, in addition to the original Derbys. An extension to the building was added in 1948 but in 1950, under the last manager, Mr Sutton, cheesemaking ended; about thirty-three farmers were at that time sending their supplies to Reapsmoor. The building still continued as a milk depot for a further two years after which its use as a dairy ceased. It has since been utilised for various storage purposes (plate, p 126).

Cheese factories at Glutton Bridge, near Earl Sterndale (Hartington Middle Quarter, SK 084666), at Gratton (SK 209616), and at Grange Mill (Ible parish, SK 244576) all dated from the same period. Wensleydale cheeses were made at the Glutton factory by Express Dairies before closure in the early 1960s; it is now a garage. The Gratton factory has been longer disused and now houses poultry, while the one at Grange Mill, built in 1875 under the patronage of the Gell family, has also long since ceased to serve its original purpose.

Only a very small part remains of the old cotton-mill warehouse at Woodeaves, near Fenny Bentley (Tissington parish, SK 184504), used for the making of Stilton cheeses for a period between 1910 and 1930 by William Nuttall, brother of John Nuttall of Hartington. And there is virtually nothing, save the wall foundations, of the United Dairies' cheese factory and milk depot at Ecton (Wetton parish, SK 096583), which occupied the site of a former smelting house.

With the vast growth of the towns surrounding the Peak District and the greater demand for liquid milk, and since the development first of railway and then of improved road transport facilities, there has, since 1900, been a considerable increase in dairy farming. But from the turn of the century cheesemaking took a definite second place. The small cheesemaking co-operatives found it difficult to compete with the prices paid for liquid milk, although the larger dairy firms which stepped in found the small-scale manufacture a useful balancing factor when supplies exceeded demands. Bigger dairy factories grew up to which milk supplies were directed, one such concern being that of Express Dairies at Rowsley (SK 259658), which itself was closed, a victim of yet further centralisation, in 1968.

AGRICULTURE TODAY

Present-day agriculture in the Peak District national park is based chiefly on grass and hill farming. There is a predominance of small owner-occupied farms; about three-quarters of the farms have less than 75 acres, two-thirds under 50. The Swaledale breed of sheep is now as populous as the Derbyshire Gritstone on the high moors while Cluns and Kerrys are the main breeds kept on the lower uplands. Dairy farming, though now somewhat declining, is in evidence on many farms on the limestone and in the valleys and also on the lower gritstone slopes, where a great deal of land has been improved in recent years by reclaiming and drainage. Some store cattle are produced by crossing the dairy cows—now mainly Friesians—with a beef bull such as the Hereford or Charollais. The hill farms run suckler herds of beef cows and these are often crossbred hardy cows again mated with the Hereford and Charollais breeds; the calves are mostly sold at the local October calf sales. In addition to farming, certain areas of the northern sector, particularly surrounding the large reservoirs, are now devoted to forestry. Amongst the difficulties present-day farmers have to face are reductions of acreages due to various types of modern development and labour losses caused by the attractions of other industries.

Notes to this chapter are on page 250

CHAPTER SEVEN

Communications

ROADS AND PACKWAYS

ALTHOUGH itself sparsely inhabited, the Peak District with its hills and dales was familiar ground to the feet of travellers from the surrounding lowland and beyond even more than 2,000 years ago. Not only was it known for the potential mineral wealth which it held but also as an upland region to be negotiated in transit from one side to the other. With their comparative disregard for gradients in favour of directness, preferring the open heights to the dangers and difficulties which often lurked in the deeper country around, the early transporters must have looked on the Peak District less as a barrier, but rather more as a link between east and west. The many who came this way sought out and soon knew by habit the drier stretches of country, the watersheds, the safest crossing places of rivers and streams, the easier slopes, the natural landmarks and the gaps to look out for as passes through the hills. A multitude of well-trodden routes became established, many of them intersecting as they crossed what are now wild and desolate moors, some of which in an earlier epoch were inhabited before the settlements grew up in the valleys.

Whatever customary minor tracks existed, it is apparent that certain major routes traversed the district from very early days. Believed to have been one such route was the old Port Way, the subject of considerable research and investigation in the 1930s and since by Mr R. W. P. Cockerton. The occurrence of the 'port' syllable in a string of place names seemed to suggest some connection between them, and their alignment pointed to a route of very direct course. Traces of ancient road have, in fact, been found to exist at places along the probable route, though land enclosure and the construction of later roads would account for much obliteration. There is a Port Way in the vicinity of the River Alport, flowing from the southern slopes of Bleaklow in Hope Woodlands, which seems to connect with the Iron Age fort on Mam Tor. From here the route ran south, supposedly near the location of Portway Mine on the border of Castleton and Peak Forest, across Bradwell Moor to Wardlow Mires, and from here to Ashford probably roughly along the line of the existing highway. After fording the Wye it certainly passed west of Bakewell, making for the crossing of the Lathkill at Alport near Youlgreave, and then continued between Robin Hood's Stride and Cratcliffe Rocks, climbed Dudwood Lane (there is a Portaway Mine at Winster) and passed to the west of Grange Mill to merge with the Chariot Way. Further recurrence of the name 'Alport' near Wirksworth (Alport Heights and Alport Stone), of a road name 'Port Way' near Cox-bench, and a thirteenth-century deed reference to Portewaye near Sandiacre would suggest the route's further continuance into Not-tinghamshire.

It is conjectured that the original meaning of 'port' is 'way', so that the use of the two words is tautological. Mr Cockerton has suggested that the route was of military use to the Romans but certainly of pre-Roman origin, owing to the many prehistoric sites which it serves. Later it was known in places as the Derby Gate or Road, if one was going south, or the Castlegate or Castleroad if going north towards the High Peak.

The Romans built a number of streets in the Peak District, at least some of which they must have used for transporting the lead they are known to have mined in the area. For the greater part their likely routes are known and often clearly traceable; sometimes they are followed by present-day roads or by walled parish boundaries, in other places they are apparent from sunken stretches of ground, or from embankments known as aggers. The Batham Gate is a Roman street which connected the bathing settlement at Buxton (Aquae Arnemetiae) with the fort called Navio, at Brough near Bradwell. North of Buxton its route is followed by the present straight road

branching off the former A624 (now A6) to Peak Dale, continuing
north-eastwards as a minor road and then as the track of a footpath
through fields in the direction of Peak Forest. Here the Roman road
crosses the A623 east of the village, just above the lower of two sharp
bends, and is then marked by a faint line across fields and by a
terraced agger before being joined by a lane for a distance across
Bradwell Moor. This lane then leaves the Batham Gate which goes on
to run concurrently with another descending through Smalldale, just
north of Bradwell village, and then with the B6049 to Brough (Stretfield Lane) to enter the fort at Navio by the south-eastern gate.

A north-eastern street through Sheffield and the fort at Temple-
borough was the Long Causeway. This seems to have emerged from
the north-eastern gate of the fort to cross the River Noe (probably by
a wooden bridge) then turned for the Beam Ford at Bamford to run
straight up towards Stanage Edge. It is possible that when the military significance of the street no longer required the direct route an
alternative way developed along Townfield Lane towards Shatton,
crossing the Rivers Noe and Derwent after they had joined at Mytham
Bridge, and ascending by Salter Lane and Hurst Clough along a
somewhat winding course near Gatehouse and Outlane Farms. From
here the exact course of the route over Stanage and the moors beyond
is open to speculation, although the reputed track was a popular
packhorse way in later times.

Connecting Navio with the Roman settlement of Melandra, near
Glossop, was the road known as Doctor's Gate, probably in origin
pre-Roman, but certainly incorporated into the Roman street system.
This strikes out northwards past Hope railway station and Fullwood
Stile Farm to cross Hope Brink west of Wooler Knoll. Then the
generally accepted route descends into the Woodlands Valley, up
which it continues, crossing the River Ashop near Hayridge Farm.
From here it runs above, and for a way follows the same route as, the
A57 Snake road, but leaves it before the climb to the summit, and
continues west-north-westwards across the peat moor by Doctor's
Gate culvert to the Shell Brook, which it follows through Mossylee to

its destination. Much of the route, marked in places by hollow ways or by terracing, is followed by footpaths.

Another Roman street led from Buxton to Manchester; the route of this for the first part lies close to the former line of the A6 (now reclassified as A5002), but where the present road bears westwards for the Long Hill the Roman route continues on a generally straight course to Whaley Bridge. A street which connected Buxton with Leek is perpetuated by the present road connecting the towns, the A54, which follows it closely over Axe Edge and for almost the whole of its way.

Discernible for much of its straight course through the Peak District is the northern section of the Romans' Derby–Buxton street, though only parts of it are followed by present roadways. From Minninglow, north of Brassington, it is marked by stone walls along parish boundaries and for ½ mile near Pikehall by a lane. At the Bull i' the Thorn Hotel it is joined for a mile by the present A515 road, but at Great Low the two divide, the Roman road passing to the east and the modern one to the west of the hill. They rejoin for ½ mile before Brierlow Bar. Here they cross, the route of the Roman road continuing on the west parallel with the A515, running at first on the same course as the present minor road and then straight on through fields.

After the Romans departed, the streets and roads which they had pioneered doubtless continued in use to a lesser extent, with some sections becoming absorbed into an already established trackway network, and others eventually forming the basis of our modern roads. Trackways, as we have seen, existed from prehistoric times, their routes generally less thrustingly direct than the Roman roads, and further ones were developed by Anglo-Saxon settlers and by the traders of medieval times. In addition to the main routes for which they were responsible it is probable that the Romans may have laid out other minor local roads; certainly there were trackways leading from villages to their respective grazing lands, stone quarries and peat beds and also to water mills from ancient times. Some of these survive in present-day lanes, but many were obliterated at the time of agricultural enclosure. A great number of the longer distance pack-ways, though disused, are, by contrast, still traceable, due to their routes lying mainly over the high uncultivated moors.

Peak District packways were evidently exceedingly numerous, the different trading routes forming an intricate web, and teams of pack-horses or mules, forty or fifty in number, were a common sight. Each animal was fitted with a special saddle with crooks attached for sup-porting a large pannier on either side; the leading horse and some-times one or more of the others also had a bell suspended from a bridle or mounted on a collar, which rang as they went along as a warning to other travellers and for guiding the rear horses during darkness. The men in charge of packhorse trains or 'jags' were known as jaggers, a word which still persists in Jaggers Clough on the border of Edale and Hope, and in Jaggers Lane, Hathersage, to give a clue to former traffic.

Many packways survive as distinct tracks over the moors, often marked as footpaths or bridleways. Often these form deep hollows resulting either from several centuries of continual use, or in some cases due to improvement works of the sixteenth century or later in which rocks or mud were removed. An example of one such hollow way can be seen in a track between Lady's Cross and Little Barbrook Reservoir on Big Moor, north-east of Baslow, an area where there is an abundance of old packways with crossings and junctions of numerous routes. Here, too, as in some other places, there are lengths paved with stone flags, no doubt to counter wet or boggy patches, probably dating from the seventeenth or eighteenth centuries.

Natural landmarks such as hills and rocky tors, and ancient features —burial mounds or crosses—guided the early travellers. Later, wooden or stone guide posts or cairns were erected at appropriate points to indicate routes. In the early eighteenth century the pro-vision of wood or stone guide posts at cross highways leading to market towns was made necessary by law, and many of the latter sort can still be seen on the moors at the junctions of old tracks, and also

K

elsewhere, some of them having been moved and re-used as field gateposts.

Where rivers or streams could not be easily forded bridges were constructed, many of which still remain. The fine bridge over the Wye at Bakewell, built in about 1300 and widened in the early nineteenth century, with its recesses in which pedestrians could take refuge from the danger of being run down by jostling pack animals, must have carried many strings of packhorses. One of smaller proportions, dating from 1664, spans the river a short distance upstream by Holme Hall at SK 215689. In the remoter areas there are a number of other delightful packhorse bridges, two of which, due to the making of reservoirs, have been dismantled and preserved by reconstruction at a higher level: the ancient one crossing the upper Derwent was removed in 1942, during construction of the Ladybower Reservoir, to a point farther upstream at Slippery Stones (SK 168951); and another, which bridged the Wildmoorstone Brook in Hartington Upper Quarter, in the area submerged by the Errwood Reservoir, was removed in the mid-1960s and re-erected a mile up the valley to carry an existing footpath over the River Goyt (SK 013732, plate, p 126).

Of the various commodities transported from or across the Peak District, lead must have been among the earliest, and it was also one of the last. Information handed down at Chelmorton recalls a scene of around 1820, with long trains of packhorses, stretching from a lead mine at the top of the village down the length of the street, standing waiting to set off with their pannier loads of lead ore for the smelters. Smelted pigs of lead in early times were carried to Nottingham and Bawtry, but after the construction of canals in the eighteenth century horse transport was used on well-worn routes only as far as the water heads at Sheffield and Chesterfield.

As far as possible transport was reciprocal. Malt was carried from the south-east through the Peak District into Cheshire and Lancashire while Cheshire salt constituted an important eastward flow. Points on salt routes can be identified by such names as Saltersford in Rainow parish, where the Todd Brook was crossed, and the six-horse teams plying between Northwich and Chesterfield were fed and rested on Salters Hill, by Salters Brook—a northern tributary of the Etherow—and by Saltergate Lane at Bamford. Lime was commonly taken back on return trips and also involved much trading within the area; South Head Farm, Hayfield, is reputed to be a place where a number of packhorses were kept for transporting lime from kilns at Bradwell to farms in the surrounding area. Hayfield was an important point on the packhorse network: a main route led eastwards by way of the Sett Valley and Edale Cross, and others climbed north-east to Yorkshire. Both lime and wool were transported to Holmfirth by way of Woodhead and Holme Moss and the horses doubtless returned with woollen goods and coal. There was two-way traffic in lime and coal between Tideswell and Sheffield in the eighteenth century, while the growth of surrounding towns caused a steady increase in the outflow of Peak District farms' food produce; milk in fact was carried into Sheffield by packhorse as late as 1870.

Besides the trade in lime and the transport of chert south-westwards to the Potteries (see Chapter Three) other stone left Peak District quarries for places far afield. Goytsclough Quarry (SK 011734), mentioned in the earlier chapter, is known to have supplied stone for use elsewhere, and its ownership by Thomas Pickford in the seventeenth century was almost certainly a contributory factor in the development of the vast Pickford's carrying business. There is a tradition that Thomas Pickford, in 1646 living at Prestbury in Cheshire, was the forerunner of the firm; in the Civil War he was accused of Royalist sympathies and his property was forfeited, and information that he supplied horses to the Cavaliers supports the likelihood of his being involved in the carrying trade. About thirty years later he reputedly owned a quarry on the Cheshire–Derbyshire borders—undoubtedly Goytsclough—and obtained a contract for supplying stone to mend roads in the district around Macclesfield, a process which merely consisted of tipping chipped stones into the dust or mud for passing traffic to consolidate. The stones were carried from the quarry by teams of packhorses and, as it occurred to Pickford that it was uneconomic for the panniers to return empty, he arranged to carry and distribute goods to people in neighbouring villages. Travelling in all weathers and staying habitually at the same inns, and no doubt bringing with him the latest news as well as the mail, Pickford became a well-known and respected figure over a wide locality. His carrying business so flourished that before long it was extended to Manchester where he apparently joined forces with other carriers already involved in long-distance journeying to London.

In the eighteenth century Pickfords' advertisements indicated their use of various London inns as headquarters, by which time waggons were in use. Advances in wheeled transport, in the form of waggon and stage coach, were helped considerably by the progressiveness of succeeding members of the Pickford family whose journeys between Manchester and London must have taken them regularly over parts of the Peak District. Pickford's waggons were built to carry heavy loads, and although progress was slow—only about 20 miles a day were covered—a six-horse waggon could carry the equivalent of thirty packhorses. Robbers were a constant hazard on journeys and the blunderbuss a necessary protective item of equipment. Waggoners were forbidden to ride in case they fell asleep, and had to walk alongside.

Roads at this time were in a deplorable state. Although some had existed and been in constant use since Anglo-Saxon days little was ever done to maintain them in good condition and their surfaces were largely mud; responsibility for upkeep rested with the respective parishes and for the most part the roads were completely neglected. With the growth of wheeled traffic in the seventeenth century and its increase during the eighteenth some attention was, however, given to bridges; new ones were built to obviate fords and narrow ones enlarged and strengthened in order to take carriageways over rivers. The older of the two present bridges across the Derwent at Baslow, close by the ancient ford, was built in 1609; in it is incorporated a watchman's building in which all able-bodied men of Baslow had to take turns to watch out for and prevent entry of undesirable characters who might come across the bridge. The widened Coldwall Bridge over the Dove at Thorpe bears the date 1726 and has a milestone on its east side with a metal plate inscribed 'Cheadle 11 miles'; the bridge is more than 100yd long and, besides its lofty span over the river, there are smaller arches for taking flood water. Coldwall Bridge, formerly gated and with a gate-post still remaining, is now virtually disused, and the line of the former coach road is just discernible from grassy tracks through the fields on either side (plate, p 143).

The need for road improvements and proper maintenance became an absolute necessity particularly with the further development of industry and the increasing transport of lead, stone and textiles. This was met by the establishment of turnpike trusts by which a number of existing roads were improved or re-graded by deviation or re-routing and new ones constructed. Under the system a group of local people were nominated by Act of Parliament as trustees for the construction and operation of a particular road on which tolls were subsequently charged to travellers and the proceeds used to cover costs and ensuing maintenance. The tolls were extracted at set points where a gate topped by a spiked frame or 'turnpike' was set up across the road together with a toll house, so constructed as to provide good visibility of oncoming vehicles for the man in charge. Though many have disappeared a number of these toll-bar cottages still remain, including well-preserved examples at Baslow (SK 267733) and at Grindleford Bridge (Nether Padley, SK 245778), and another, a stone building less obviously recognisable as such, at a three-crossway just west of Monyash village (SK 147665). The turnpike roads were also marked by milestones, of uniform style for a particular section, some of stone and others—particularly later ones—of metal.

Amongst the earliest of such roads were the Nottingham–Newhaven, divided into four districts, and the Chesterfield–Hernstone Lanehead turnpike system, all of 1759. Of the four districts of the Nottingham–Newhaven turnpike the first, of a total length of 31½ miles, entered the Peak District from Matlock and passed through Snitterton, Wensley and Winster before reaching Newhaven. The third of them, of $15\frac{3}{4}$ miles, ran from Wirksworth via Cromford, Matlock, Bakewell to Headstone Head, Monsal Dale. The turnpike from Chesterfield through Baslow to Tideswell (Hernstone Lane-head) threw off a branch through Bakewell and Conksbury to Newhaven and took over a short length of the Port Way or Derby Gate from the Shutts hollow to the Two Trees (SK 216662), where the turnpike road turned westwards to cross the River Lathkill by the sixteenth-century Conksbury Bridge.

Further turnpikes authorised by Acts of the eighteenth century were those from Sheffield to Baslow via Owler Bar and from Hathersage to Baslow. Others at the same period led to Buxton from Ashbourne and Macclesfield, and from Manchester by way of Whaley Bridge. The latter included the Long Hill just north of Buxton, where the road was re-routed to take a wider loop around a valley, reducing the gradient, as described by Farey, from $6\frac{1}{4}$ to $1\frac{1}{10}$in per yd: the track of the old road is plainly visible taking the shorter but steeper course, to the west of the present road. Important turnpikes of the early nineteenth century included the road through the Wye Valley from Ashford to Buxton—now the A6—and the one from Sheffield to Chapel-en-le-Frith connecting with Macclesfield. Adding a further route across the Pennines to the already turnpiked Woodhead road, was that from Sheffield to Glossop via the Snake Pass (A57), on which construction proceeded following an Act of 1818; while in the extreme north the Greenfield–Holmfirth road (A635) was developed as a turnpike following an Act of 1824.

Growth of the railways drew traffic away from the roads. The turnpike system continued in operation until the second half of the nineteenth century but by an Act of 1878 turnpikes as such were abolished and 'main roads' created. Responsibility for upkeep for a time reverted to the parishes but was later taken over by the county councils on their formation in 1888.

Thus, although some became down-graded to the status of minor roads, the turnpikes in general set the pattern of the system of road communications which exists in the national park today. Their influence in the development of the area's industrial potential was considerable.

RAILWAYS

The area covered by the Peak District National Park has never been actually penetrated by any canals, although two reached almost to its boundaries—the Cromford Canal opened in February 1792, and the Peak Forest Canal (see Chapter Three, p 65) opened in May 1800. There were various proposals for the construction of waterways to link the two, but none of them ever materialised; the lifting which would have been necessary to raise navigation to summit levels and the general difficulties of maintaining a water supply in the intervening limestone country rendered the proposed schemes impracticable.

The Cromford & High Peak

Eventually it was decided to link the two canals by a railway, the Cromford & High Peak, which, with its steep inclined planes at least shared some of the characteristics of actual canal building of the time. Besides linking the industrial districts on either side, the objects were to provide outgoing transport for lime and other minerals, and for agricultural products, and to bring in supplies of coal and other commodities to the remoter areas. Richard Arkwright was one of the subscribers to the scheme and Josias Jessop was employed as engineer. Jessop estimated the cost as £155,080, including £20,000 for the stationary engines needed for the inclined planes; the actual cost amounted to about £180,000. The Cromford & High Peak Railway was incorporated by an Act of 2 May 1825 which authorised construction of the railway, 33 miles 70 chains in length, on which wagons were to be 'propelled by stationary or locomotive steam engines or other sufficient power'. Capital was fixed at £164,000 in £100 shares, and loans of £32,880 secured on a mortgage of the undertaking. In 1827 a branch to Ashbourne was proposed at an additional cost of about £18,000 which would have meant cheaper coal for the town, but funds did not permit its construction.

The C & HP, which, for nearly half its total length ran through the area of today's national park, was opened from Cromford Wharf to Hurdlow on 29 May 1830, and from Hurdlow to Whaley Bridge on 6 July 1831. But it was not a paying proposition, and succeeding years were fraught with financial difficulties. Efforts to alleviate the situation resulted in further Acts of 1843, 1855 and 1858. The Act of 1855 also provided for construction of a link with the Stockport, Disley & Whaley Bridge Railway (connection had already been made from Cromford Wharf with the Manchester, Buxton, Matlock & Midlands Junction Railway at High Peak Junction) and for a slight deviation between Ladmanlow and the south end of Burbage Tunnel, and gave the company power to act as carriers of passengers. By a fifth Act, of 1862, the C & HP was leased retrospectively from 25 March 1861 to the London & North Western Railway Company by which it was worked until 30 June 1887; it then became amalgamated with the London & North Western, the C & HP being dissolved.

Another Act, obtained in 1890, authorised the improvement of the line between the top of Hopton incline and Hurdlow, including re-alignment, and construction of new lines from Ashbourne to Parsley Hay and Hindlow to Buxton. Abandonment of the C & HP line north of Ladmanlow was also provided for, except for a short length at Whaley Bridge leading to the goods yard at the foot of the Shallcross incline.

Rising from an altitude of 278ft at the Cromford Canal to 1,266ft at the top of the Hurdlow incline, and falling to 517ft at Whaley Bridge, the original line had a total of nine inclined planes. Five took the railway from Cromford to the summit (Sheep Pasture lower and upper, Middleton, Hopton and Hurdlow) and four effected the descent (Bunsall upper and lower Goyt, Shallcross and Whaley Bridge). The Hurdlow incline had the greatest length, of 850yd, but with only 160ft vertical rise; the two at Bunsall were the steepest, the

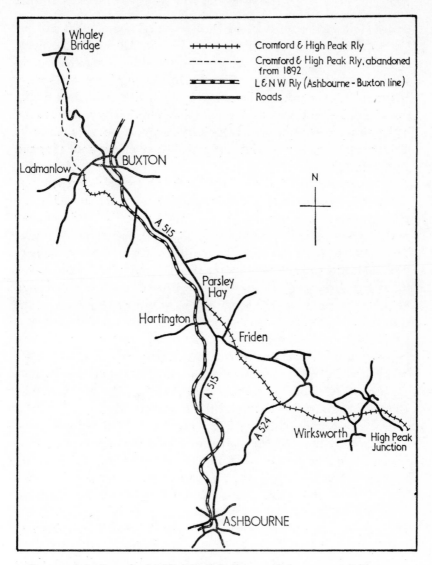

Routes of the Cromford & High Peak Railway and the L & NWR Ashbourne–
Buxton line

upper Goyt incline, 660yd long, had a vertical rise of 266ft and the lower Goyt, 455yd in length, a rise of 191ft. All the inclines were originally powered by steam engines, assisted by counterbalance in some cases, except the one at Whaley Bridge which was worked by counterbalance alone. Chains were used on all the inclines at the start, but all except those at Hopton and Whaley Bridge were replaced by hemp ropes in 1855–7 and these by wire ropes from 1861 onwards. Chains continued in use at Hopton and Whaley Bridge until 1877 and 1952 respectively.

Motive power on the almost level sections between the inclines was provided by horses until steam locomotives were introduced on 20 January 1841. After this, horses still continued to be used, possibly until 1855. A deviation of the line at Hurdlow, opened on 2 January 1869, enabled the locomotives to run direct from Hopton incline to Ladmanlow. Until the Act of 1855 the company was not authorised for carrying passengers, but this was licensed to Messrs German Wheatcroft who from 1833 operated a passenger carriage daily on the line. After the company took over, a limited passenger service, comprising a single compartment on a goods train, continued until 1877.

Between Cromford and Buxton the railway continued in use for mineral traffic to a decreasing extent until the 1960s, with final closure on 2 October 1967. Plans are currently under negotiation by Derbyshire County Council and the Peak Park Planning Board for converting a section of the track to a 'green way' amenity for walkers. There are a number of interesting features in the portion within the national park. North-west of Minninglow, at SK 195582, is a very striking high embankment entirely faced with limestone. This section of the line, as far as Friden, following closely the natural contours, is noted for its severe curves; three were of 3 chains radius and the Gotham curve was of only 2½ chains. The Newhaven Tunnel beneath the A515 road (SK 151629), just south of the junction with the Ashbourne line at Parsley Hay station, has a length of 51yd; above the south portal is a stone plaque bearing the company's name surrounding a wagon, the contractor's initials and the date 1825, and on the north is another depicting the railway's crest and the names of the engineer and clerk (plate, p 143). After Hurdlow station the course of the earlier route (abandoned from 2 January 1869) can be seen bearing away to the west to the ascent of Hurdlow incline (marked by a line of electric pylons); the two converge again after the line passes out of the park to serve quarries in the Buxton area. North of Buxton the section of the line abandoned from 27 June 1892 is seen again in the national park on its emergence from the 580yd long Burbage Tunnel (SK 031740), which is now blocked. From here its meandering, then straighter course northwards on the eastern side of the Goyt Valley can still be discerned, including the Bunsall incline which was made into a road during the construction of the Errwood Reservoir in the 1960s (SK 021753).

The Sheffield, Ashton-under-Lyne & Manchester

A few years after the opening of the Cromford & High Peak Railway, work was in progress farther north on a line—later a part of the Great Central Railway—which was to provide the first rail link between Manchester and Sheffield. On this route the great barrier of the Pennines was overcome by construction of the 3 mile 13yd long Woodhead Tunnel (SK 113999–156022, plate, p 144), 1,000ft in altitude, more than 500ft deep beneath the wild windswept gritstone moors, but at the cost of notorious degradation and danger for the navvies involved. Construction of the line by the Sheffield, Ashton-under-Lyne & Manchester Railway Company, formed in 1835, was authorised by an Act of 1837, and in 1839 work on the tunnel commenced; £60,000 was the original estimated cost, a figure which was to rise to £200,000 during the course of construction. The tunnel took six years to make and during this time hundreds of men were employed. At one stage 1,500 or more were involved working simultaneously from each end and on the five ventilation shafts, the longest shaft 579ft in depth.

A vivid account of the tunnel's construction has been given by Mr

Terry Coleman in his book *The Railway Navvies* (1965). During it the men lived in encampments on the hillside above; at first they slept in the open but when winter set in they built for themselves primitive shelters of stone in which they dwelt in squalid fashion. Many of the early recruits were specially selected and of good type, but as the need for labour increased and more were taken on standards became tougher and rougher. Working in such isolation and discomfort in any case demanded men who were hard and not too fastidious. Pay was high but infrequent and it was soon gone; days of drunkenness followed the bi-monthly pay-days and the men were exploited by high prices charged for provisions in the contractor-controlled shops, the sole source of supply in the remote district. The work itself was laborious and dangerous in the extreme. Not only was continuous blasting necessary but, due to the geological structure, all except 1,000yd of the length had to be masonry lined. To make matters worse, because of shortages of money inadequate safety precautions were taken, resulting in frequent accidents; when the single-line tunnel was opened on 23 December 1845 it was at the cost of thirty-two lives and countless injuries.

In 1847, when the Sheffield, Ashton-under-Lyne & Manchester Railway Company was absorbed in the Manchester, Sheffield & Lincolnshire Railway Company, work commenced on an adjacent tunnel to take the up line. This was slightly less tough going than the first tunnel since rock conditions were known and the five ventilation shafts as well as twenty-five interconnecting side arches had already been made. But although accidents were fewer the labour force was struck by cholera which caused twenty-eight deaths. The second Woodhead Tunnel was opened on 2 February 1852.

For a century the two tunnels continued in use, control passing to the London & North Eastern Railway in 1923 until nationalisation. After World War II a third tunnel was constructed immediately south of the other two to take both up and down lines. This was completed in 1954 and still carries the now electrified trains. The two early tunnels were then relegated to disuse until, in the 1960s, the second of them—the former up line—was taken over for an un-precedented civil and electrical engineering scheme. This resulted from the routing of the electrical supergrid across the Pennines from Thorpe Marsh near Doncaster to Stalybridge in Cheshire and objec-tions, raised at a public enquiry at Barnsley in 1963 by the Peak Park Planning Board and amenity bodies, to the erection of overhead power lines over the skyline of the high moorland between Dunford Bridge and Woodhead. A less expensive alternative to conventional underground cabling existed in the form of the available idle tunnel, which the Central Electricity Generating Board subsequently acquired.

Extensive renovation was needed in this tunnel, which is semi-elliptical in shape like its adjacent twin, 14ft 6in wide at the base and 17ft 6in high, to make it suitable for its modern use. Thick accumula-tions of soot were a great problem; hosing was ruled out since drainage leads into the River Etherow which feeds Manchester Cor-poration's reservoirs, and vacuuming proved unsuccessful. Eventually high-pressure air jets were used to blow off the soot—a filthy job for the men concerned as breathing masks became rapidly clogged. On settling, the soot was neutralised with lime, incorporated with cement into the old railway ballast and damped to set into a hard floor. Considerable repair was necessary to the walls; water pressure behind the stonework had caused distortion and the pointing had suffered from water and sulphurous fumes. Remedial work was done by in-jecting cement grout into the spaces behind the stones and providing weep holes, and a special machine tackled the large area of repointing. Along one side of the length of the new floor the power cables have been laid in trefoil formation in a double concrete trough, in section like an E on its back. These are water-cooled, and there are weirs at intervals since there is a fall of 85ft from one end of the tunnel to the other. Cable joints on top of the trough are air-cooled by electric fans at the tunnel entrances. Parallel to the trough is a 2ft narrow-gauge railway used during the recent construction work and retained for maintenance.

No further use has been found for the first Woodhead Tunnel, the middle one of the three; black, dripping and eerie, the subterranean atmosphere now clear of the choking fumes which formerly pervaded it, the tunnel lies dormant as a sepulchral refuge for the ghosts of unfortunate navvies and of steam-hissing clattering trains.

The Midland

Farther south, companies which by amalgamation were incorporated in the Midland Railway had reached the edge of the Peak District by the middle of the nineteenth century, the line from Ambergate having extended as far as Rowsley in 1849 on a projected route to Manchester. At this stage, however, there were difficulties. The Duke of Devonshire would not permit the line to continue up the Derwent Valley through Chatsworth and the Duke of Rutland objected to its passing Haddon Hall. Eventually agreement was reached for the making of a tunnel beneath Haddon park, to the east of the Wye and at a higher level, and, under the Midland Company's Act of 25 May 1860, construction of the line progressed. A second station was made at Rowsley and the railway from here through Bakewell to Hassop opened for passengers on 1 August 1862. Work continued on the line, which rejoined the Wye Valley by the spectacular Monsal Dale viaduct and skilfully negotiated the tortuous limestone gorge by a number of tunnels as far as Buxton, to which a passenger service opened on 1 June 1863 (plate, p 144). From an intermediate junction at Miller's Dale the making of the railway pressed on northwards through Great Rocks and Dove Holes Dales to New Mills and Manchester which was reached in 1867. Sadly, during the 1950s and sixties all the stations on the section within the national park were closed one by one, the last being Bakewell on 1 July 1968, and the line which connected Buxton with Derby and London and which for a century provided an important direct route to Manchester is now disused. The future of the abandoned track is as yet undecided although consideration is being given to its possible development as an amenity.

Much later in the nineteenth century, in 1893, the Midland Railway, on completion of the Cowburn and Totley Tunnels, opened its line from Chinley to Dore & Totley which provided an additional link between Manchester and Sheffield and brought new life and opportunities to the Edale and Hope Valleys. The line continues to operate although station facilities have been reduced.

The London & North Western

Another railway constructed at the end of the nineteenth century was the London & North Western line from Buxton to Ashbourne. Work on this was in progress during the early 1890s and involved a new section of railway from Buxton to Hindlow and another from Parsley Hay to Ashbourne. Between Hindlow and Parsley Hay the line ran concurrently with the 1869 deviation of the former Cromford & High Peak which by this time had already become a part of the LNWR. The northern section was completed first and was opened from Buxton to Parsley Hay for goods traffic in June 1892 and for passengers from 1 June 1894. From Parsley Hay to Ashbourne the line was opened for all traffic on 4 August 1899 and on the same date a loop bypassing Buxton station but connecting the Ashbourne line with the company's already existing railway from Buxton to Whaley Bridge and Manchester was also put into use.

The route of the railway takes a meandering course northwards from Ashbourne, climbing through the open limestone countryside from an altitude of 500–1,000ft, and keeping close company with the A515 road about which it twists and turns. During its life the railway was used by passengers and to a large extent for the transport of limestone from quarries en route and for agricultural goods. The line was closed to passenger traffic on 1 November 1954 but continued to carry goods until the last-used stations, Hartington and Hindlow, closed in 1964. During its final years, however, the railway was used occasionally for excursions and as an emergency passenger service in times of severe winter weather until 7 October 1963.

During the 1960s, 11½ miles of the railway south from Hartington were purchased by the Peak Park Planning Board and adapted for use as a public amenity called the 'Tissington Trail' for walking, pony trekking and other pursuits. The old track was removed, soil laid and grass seed sown and attention given to the derelict stations. Both Tissington and Alsop-en-le-Dale stations which were of wood have been completely demolished and at these, as well as at Hartington, car parks have been provided. The former signal box at Hartington has been retained as a briefing room for the warden and a railway cottage for his dwelling. It is planned eventually to extend the trail northwards to Parsley Hay, to link there with the projected scheme for the route of the Cromford & High Peak.

The Leek & Manifold

The last railway constructed within the national park's area and the one with the shortest life was the Leek & Manifold Valley Light Railway which ran up the valleys of the Rivers Hamps and Manifold from Waterhouses to Hulme End. The idea of a narrow-gauge railway for opening up and developing this remote and hilly part of Staffordshire was proposed by a consortium of local business men following the passing of the Light Railways Act of 1896. It was thought that the new line would be of untold value for the transport of milk and other agricultural produce, for carrying stone from quarries in the locality and lead and copper from a hoped-for mining revival, and also as a tourist attraction. But the enthusiasm and optimism were unrewarded, for in operation the line proved to be a financial failure.

The promoters' application to the Light Railway Commissioners was approved, and an order made for the railway's construction on 6 March 1899. The company started with capital of £15,000 in £1 shares with power to increase to £20,000, aided by a Government grant of £10,000 and a loan from Staffordshire County Council of £10,000 at 3 per cent. Later the Treasury added £7,500 to its gift and made a loan of similar amount.

Joseph Forsyth was appointed engineer for the 2ft 6in gauge line. It was agreed that on completion the North Staffordshire Railway should work and maintain it, receiving 55 per cent of gross returns. A common seal depicting Thor's Cave, a feature seen on the route, was designed by Sir Thomas Wardle, one of the nine original directors.

After prolonged discussions and disagreements over precise routing the scheme was inaugurated by the Duke of Devonshire who ceremonially cut the first sod at Waterhouses on 3 October 1899. But there were further delays before actual construction could begin. Earl Cathcart demanded facilities at Beeston Tor for tenants on his estate which led to the provision of a bridge over the Hamps from the Throwley track and a road to Grindon station, and in 1900 a report to the directors indicated faults in the line's specifications. Advice was sought of Mr E. R. Calthrop, an engineer with experience of light railways in India; in his estimation considerable reduction in construction costs were possible and he was shortly appointed engineer in place of Forsyth, who had died. Calthrop's actual expenditure of £35,944 saved £11,000 on the original estimate, and at no detriment to the line which needed no replacement throughout its thirty years of use.

Work started in March 1902 and in spite of a smallpox epidemic amongst the workmen was completed in two years. The line was opened on 27 June 1904 but the standard-gauge railway from Leek, with which it was to connect at Waterhouses, was not ready until 1 July 1905. Meanwhile a temporary station was provided by the level crossing east of Waterhouses village from where Leek passengers could continue the journey by steam bus.

The Indian-type trains designed by Calthrop comprised two 2-6-4 tank engines named respectively 'E. R. Calthrop' and 'J. B. Earle' (after the resident engineer), carriages of open saloon type with platforms at the ends, covered and open wagons, and transporters which could be transferred to the standard gauge at Waterhouses.

The early years of running were neither harmonious for the directors nor lucrative. By 1907, when two daily trains were running

L

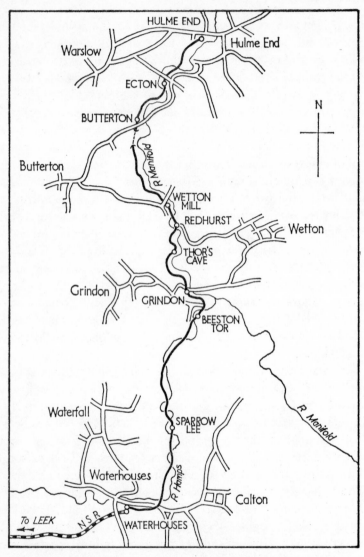

Route of the Leek & Manifold Valley Light Railway

each way in winter and three in summer, (with a travelling letter box introduced in 1906), plus extras at holiday times, finances were in a serious plight. With no prospect for extension to Longnor and Buxton which could have helped, the railway struggled on until 1914 when war added to the difficulties. The Treasury refused to waive its loan, the bank pressed for settlement, and donations were necessary to settle the company's overdraft.

In 1921 the railway became a part of the LMS but suffered the competition of improving road facilities. Milk transport was a vital asset of those last years; two glass-lined milk tankers travelled each night from the dairy at Ecton to London, and milk churns were carried too. But in 1932 Ecton dairy closed and lorries were in use for taking churns to local factories. A decision was made to close the railway, and the last train ran on 10 March 1934.

When demolition was planned, use of the line as a footpath was suggested, and purchase by Staffordshire County Council was urged. Eventually the LMS presented the track by deed of gift to the SCC, and the council converted it to a hard-surfaced footpath at a cost of £6,000. On 23 July 1937 this road was opened from Hulme End as far as the A523 Leek–Ashbourne road, the remaining section into Waterhouses village being abandoned. The stretch between Redhurst and Butterton, which includes the Swainsley Tunnel, was opened as a motor road with passing places in 1953. Station buildings along the line have been removed but at Hulme End the former station yard is now a car park; fences and gates and the original steel bridges still remain.

The route today throughout its length of $8\frac{1}{2}$ miles provides extremely easy if somewhat over-macadamised walking. The railway atmosphere seems to have departed, but the scenery is unchanged and is still as delightful and inviting as when the sedately moving trains (30mph was the limit) brought parties of holidaymakers up the valley from Leek and the Potteries.

Notes to this chapter are on page 251

PART TWO

Gazetteer

SITES already referred to in Part One are included here, as well as many others. It is possible that changes may have occurred in some places since the various features were last seen and recorded, and the author would welcome information on these and on any interesting sites which may have been omitted.

For the sake of consistency, and since many readers are likely to have ordnance survey maps at hand for locating the map references, the area is dealt with strictly in parishes. Where difficulties are likely to arise due to a familiar place name not in itself being a parish, the name is included and the reader directed to the appropriate entry. The national park boundary is rigidly observed in the Gazetteer (see explanation, p 25) and where only part of a parish lies within the park the extent is indicated following the parish name. Exclusion of a very few parishes or part-parishes from the list indicates their apparent lack of any industrial archaeological remains.

It should be emphasised that the inclusion of a place in this list does not necessarily imply that the public have free access, nor that an owner or occupier may be willing to give permission for viewing.

ABNEY & ABNEY GRANGE

Smelting. Smelting is said to have been carried out on Abney Low, and the names 'Burton Bole' and 'Smelting Hill' in the north of the parish suggest it was also done there.

Agriculture. Walled fields north-west of the village are believed to have been strips of open field arable until enclosed in the nineteenth century.

There was formerly a pinfold at Abney Grange, dismantled for its stone during living memory.

ALDWARK

Mining. A number of old shafts are said to be remains of early lead mining.

ALLGREAVE—see WINCLE

ALPORT—see YOULGREAVE; HARTHILL

ALSOP-EN-LE-DALE—see EATON & ALSOP

ALSTONFIELD

Quarrying. There are a number of small limestone quarries, and a limekiln beneath a large mound at SK 113573.

Mills. West Side Corn Mill (SK 101589) on the River Manifold, bears the date 1667; it is now used for agricultural purposes and all associations with milling have disappeared, except for a millstone incorporated into a side doorway and the still traceable leat. Lode Mill (SK 146551) on the River Dove, another former corn mill, also now forms part of a farm; remains of the waterwheel and of the old mill machinery, last used early this century, are still in position. Downstream at Milldale (SK 139547) is the site of another mill, long demolished; a millstone lies on the ground and there are remains of the weir and short mill race.

Flax-weaving. A house in the village (SK 129558) is said to have been used for the purpose, see p 115.

ASHFORD IN THE WATER

Mining. Considerable lead-mining remains, particularly in the west of the parish, include Magpie Mine (SK 172682) which is said to have been worked over 300 years. The site is best approached from Sheldon village. Dominating feature of the mine is the Cornish engine house which has the main shaft on one side and a round chimney on the other. To the north-east of the engine house are remains of wooden jigs used in the 1950s and slightly farther away, on the same side, the remains of the round powder store. Due south of the engine house, beside the entrance from the Monyash road, is the former black-smith's shop, weigh house and dwelling house; these now comprise the Field Centre of the Peak District Mines Historical Society which is tenant of the property. Building remains on the western side include those of a whimsey (steam-driven winding engine) house dating from about 1830, and a building in which stood a horizontal engine in-stalled in 1870, with its boiler house adjoining. From this building the remains of an underground flue can be seen, leading to an old square chimney stack which, it is believed, may have previously served an early steam whimsey engine (plate, p 17). Between these buildings and the Cornish engine house are corrugated metal sheds dating from the 1950s and steel headgear which replaced the former wooden structure at the same time. There are over twenty open shafts surrounding the site and remains of gin circles and a crushing circle can also be seen. The limestone-lined drain which took away water raised by the pumps can be seen on the west side. (See also p 45.) Mogshaw Mine (SK 183679) is a very old mine; it was worked for lead up to the nineteenth century and during the present one for barytes. True Blue Mine (SK 178680) was worked in the latter part of the nineteenth century and for a period from 1913 in conjunction with Magpie.

Domesday Book records a lead works at Ashford.

Quarrying. Quarries include those worked for black marble, the Arrock Quarry (SK 191694), and in Rookery Plantation (SK 190695).

Old chert quarry at SK 193695.

Mills. Flewitt's Corn Mill (SK 198695), believed to be ancient, was owned by the Duke of Devonshire until the 1950s; leats from the River Wye pass on either side of the mill which formerly had two waterwheels, a wooden one of which parts remain and one of iron which is now removed. Corn is still ground at the mill by water-powered turbines which have been in use many years; seven sets of millstones and the old wooden gearing still remain within the building. The former mill house is now a private dwelling.

The site of the former marble mill, later used for barytes and for timber (SK 190694) is now occupied by the North Derbyshire Water Board (see p 75). Immediately downstream on the same site are the ruins of the former comb mill, see p 100 (plate, p 71).

Agriculture. The pinfold, formerly situated to the south of the village, was swept away by construction of the A6 bypass.

The sheepwash (SK 194696) is described on p 150 (plate, p 125).

Communications. Part of the disused Midland Railway line and of the 533yd long Headstone Tunnel are in the north of the parish.

BAKEWELL

Mining. There are remains of lead mining in the western part of the parish including workings at Green Cowden and below Burton Moor Edge. The name Bole Hill (SK 184676) indicates a probable one-time smelting place.

Domesday Book records a lead works at Bakewell.

Quarrying. Gritstone was quarried on the eastern side of the parish, limestone on the west. Ball Cross Quarry (SK 226695) and others in Wicksop Woods and along Bakewell Edge supplied much gritstone for local building use, while limestone workings in the vicinity of Stanedge Lane also supplied stone for building as well as for lime-burning; there are remains of a limekiln at SK 212685.

Marble was extracted at the Blackstone Hollow Quarry (SK 200678) and was worked at a mill on the Wye, near Bakewell Bridge (SK 220686), see p 76.

For the two chert quarries, Holme Bank (SK 213692) and Pretoria (SK 210681), see p 78.

Brickworks. Hollows in a field beside Gypsy or Brickfield Lane

(SK 221700), mark the site of a former brickworks known as the Birchill Tileyard, owned by the Duke of Devonshire. Working was in progress in 1850 but probably finished 1875–80.

Mills. The Victoria Corn Mill beside the Buxton road (SK 216687) probably occupies the site of a mill recorded at Bakewell in Domesday Book. The large gritstone building with its iron-framed windows, dating from the late eighteenth and early nineteenth centuries, formerly belonged to the Duke of Rutland; it was rented by Messrs Bailey from about 1890 and owned by them from around 1920. Powered by water from the River Wye, the mill was used for grinding corn for local farmers up to the end of World War II and afterwards as a store for feeding stuffs. Plans are afoot by new owners for restoration of the 16ft diameter, 13ft 6in wide iron undershot waterwheel and for the mill pond; the tail race forms a pleasant feature beside the footpath which connects Milford with Castle Street.

Lumford Mill (SK 212691), formerly Arkwright's cotton mill and more recently a battery works, is discussed on pp 105–6, 109.

New or Arkwright's Square (SK 216686), immediately south-west of the Milford Hotel, consists of limestone-built cottages, originally for mill workers, grouped around a central courtyard with an arched entry (plate, p 89).

Progress Works, on the west side of the Buxton road (SK 216687) was constructed by Arkwright in about 1820 as an inn; it was at this time that the road was cut through here instead of making the loop past the present Milford House Hotel. For a time the building was used by Chesterfield Brewery as a storage centre. During World War I it became Rogers' factory for knitted wear; it is now disused.

Timber yard. There was formerly a timber works (Messrs Norman's) to the west of Matlock Street, behind the Methodist Church. After a fire this was removed to the site of the present timber yard, now Messrs Smith's, beside the Wye (SK 220685); a turbine is still in existence here but not in general use.

Tannery. There was formerly a tannery between Matlock Street and Butts Road.

Ropewalks. There was formerly a ropewalk near Endcliffe Quarry, on the north-west side of the town, and another (Matleys) inside the wall beside the A6 (SK 221679).

Agriculture. Lynchets can be seen in various fields on the west of the town with particularly good examples in a field to the north of the Monyash road (SK 213684), see plate, p 108.

The pinfold was to the south of the Monyash road (SK 212682); its site is now marked by a stone shed.

Sheep were formerly washed in the corn mill stream near Holme Bridge (SK 215689) (plate, p 125) and below the iron bridge over the Wye (SK 220683), where there was an ancient ford.

Communications. The five-arched gritstone bridge, built in about 1300 and widened in the early nineteenth century, spans the Wye at SK 219686. There is a smaller seventeenth-century packhorse bridge upstream near Holme Hall (SK 215689).

The disused Midland Railway line passes through the eastern part of the parish, with the former Bakewell station, closed to passengers on 6 March 1967 and for goods traffic on 1 July 1968, at SK 222690.

BALLIDON

Quarrying. There are various disused limestone quarries including Royston Grange Quarry (SK 204570), and also a limekiln beside the A524 road (SK 211544). (The modern large Ballidon Quarry has been developed since about 1950.)

Sand and clay quarried at Minninglow (SK 202575) was formerly used for brickmaking.

Communications. The route of the Derby–Buxton Roman road is marked by stone walls on the parish's eastern boundary.

The track of the disused Cromford & High Peak Railway passes through the north-eastern part of the parish, where it served Royston Grange and Minninglow Quarries; features include sharp curves and the limestone embankment at SK 195582 (see p 170).

BAMFORD

Quarrying. There are various old millstone grit quarry workings along Bamford Edge.

Mill. Bamford Mill (SK 205833), formerly a cotton mill on the site of an earlier corn mill, now owned by the Carbolite Company, is dealt with on page 112.

Water. Part of the Ladybower Reservoir lies within the parish, as do houses at Yorkshire Bridge built for resettling residents of the submerged villages of Derwent and Ashopton, and a section of the railway track constructed for transport of stone during building of the Howden and Derwent dams (see pp 134–6).

Communications. Bamford station was closed for goods traffic on 31 January 1966.

BASLOW & BUBNELL

Smelting. Ruins of former lead-smelting mill west of the Barbrook (SK 268734), see p 49.

Quarrying. A quarry at SK 262736 which produced a soft type of millstone grit was worked for local use up to the late 1930s.

Gardom's Edge was one of the principal millstone cutting areas (see p 82).

Coal. There are remains of old coal workings west of Robin Hood (SK 278722).

Mills. Hodgkinson's Corn Mill, which had a bakehouse adjoining, was on the Derwent below the weir (SK 250724); there was almost no mill race, the water being fed direct from the weir. The waterwheel was removed in the 1930s and the premises now comprise a dwelling and storage building.

Marples' Corn Mill (SK 272721) was in use as such in the 1880s but by 1900 was a sawmill. The altered building still remains, now the Heathylee pumping station of the North Derbyshire Water Board.

Textiles. Up to the early nineteenth century Bubnell was a centre of framework knitting for the hosiery trade.

Hatmaking formerly flourished in the parish.

Pinfold. Nothing now remains of the pinfold, which was on the south-west side of the green at Over End (SK 256725).

Communications. The site of an ancient ford across the River Derwent can still be seen, with a sloping way leading down to it beside the church. Beside it is the bridge of 1609 which incorporates a watchman's building (SK 251723), see p 164. From the crossing of the river the old road led up through Over End and Baslow Bar to the moors; above the edge the way to Chesterfield proceeded to the right and that for Sheffield along the tops of Baslow, Curbar and Froggatt Edges.

Toll bar cottage on the Sheffield–Baslow turnpike (SK 267733).

BEELEY

Smelting. Lead smelting was done at various points on Beeley Edge.

Quarrying. There was formerly much quarrying of millstone grit for both building purposes and the making of grindstones and whetstones on Beeley Moor.

Communications. Various packhorse routes crossed Beeley Moor and there are a number of early guide posts.

BIGGIN—see HARTINGTON NETHER QUARTER

BIRCHOVER

Quarrying. Millstone grit has been quarried in the parish for many years for use in the making of grinding and crushing stones as well as for building (see p 85).

Mill. Eagle Tor Mill, believed to have been an ancient one, formerly stood at SK 232627. The mill, which had previously been worked by Messrs Johnson and unused for a number of years, was demolished in the 1950s. Only the silted mill-pond remains.

BLACKWELL

Quarrying. Both Topley Pike Quarry (part of which lies within the parish) and Calton Hill Quarry (SK 119715) are modern. The latter, worked for basalt for use as road material, was opened in 1906 and closed in 1969.

Mill. The former Blackwell Corn Mill (SK 113727), disused since before living memory, has now virtually disappeared but the weir can still be seen across the River Wye.

Agriculture. 'Celtic fields' on Hall Green Farm (SK 131731) are visible from the Wormhill road (see p 137).

Communications. Parts of the disused Midland Railway line, including the 401yd long Chee Tor No 1 tunnel are in the north of the parish.

BLORE WITH SWINSCOE (Northern half of parish)

Quarrying. A disused limestone quarry and large pudding-pie kiln, with bricked arch and stone-lined basin, are at SK 126495. They have not been used in living memory.

BONSALL (Western section)

Mining. On the part of Bonsall Moor lying within the national park are numerous lead mining undulations and remains of old shafts covering almost all the ground, arising from workings on a flat vein.

The premises of the Via Gellia Colour Company Ltd at SK 278573 was formerly a lead smelting works and there are remains of flues ascending the hillside.

Quarrying. There are considerable remains of limestone quarrying, particularly alongside the Via Gellia.

BRADFIELD   (All of the parish except the extreme east)

Mining and Quarrying. Deposits of fireclay occurring in the parish
have been extracted by both underground and opencast workings in
various places, including Messrs J. & J. Dyson's Wheatshire Mine
(SK 251901) and the Ughill Mine (SK 259904) of Messrs Thomas
Wragg & Sons (see p 93). Coal has been mined on a small scale (see
p 92).

The quarrying of millstone grit has been important in the parish
and there are a number of old quarries, mainly now disused. Most
were for building stone and for the making of kerb-stones, as for
example Tor Quarry (SK 249912). Slates were cut at Thornseat Delf
(SK 229927) and also stones for engine beds until cement replaced
their use. Millstone grit is at present worked for building stone at
Loadfield Quarries (SK 257949) and gannister has been extracted in
the same area.

Mills. The former Low Bradfield Corn Mill (SK 264918) was
burnt down in 1940. Apart from the weir and mill race, and the
discernible area of the mill-pond, some pieces of ruined walling are
all that remain. Farther north there was another mill, submerged by
construction of the Broomhead Reservoir.

Water. Parts of the Langsett and Broomhead Reservoirs (SK
210000 and 260959) and the Agden (SK 260925), Strines (SK
230905), Dale Dike (SK 240915) and Damflask (SK 280907)
Reservoirs lie within the parish (see pp 128–9).

Pinfold. The large square pinfold is beside the Sheffield road
(SK 269923), see p 142.

BRADWELL

Mines and Smelting. There are considerable remains of lead mining
on Bradwell Moor, including Moss Rake and Shuttle Rake, and to
the north (plate, p 18). A former mine east of the village (SK

177810), where there is now a water pumping house, was sunk into the limestone through the overlying millstone grit.

For details of Bradwell cupolas, including the 'Slag Works' (SK 174808), see p 51.

Quarrying. The large limestone quarry in Pindale (SK 160823) closed in 1955; limeburning was previously also done here, and also, up to about 1900, at the quarries in Bradwell Dale (SK 172805) which closed in the 1930s. Quarrying continues in the north of the parish.

Mills and other industries. An old mill called Bump Mill (bump being a coarse kind of cotton), dating from the eighteenth century, was at SK 176817, but has long been demolished.

Former sawmill at SK 174811 (see p 99) and tannery at SK 174812 (see p 120).

Hatmaking was an important industry in Bradwell; the last of about six hatting shops was a house at SK 176809 (see p 123).

Telescopes, opera glasses and spectacles were a minor local industry during the nineteenth century; one of the businesses, that of Messrs Evans Bros, established in 1862, was housed in a former chapel building at Brookside (SK 174811).

Pinfold. The former pinfold at SK 172811 no longer exists, its site having been incorporated into the roadway.

Communications. The route of the Batham Gate Roman road runs over Bradwell Moor and descends through Smalldale (see p 159).

BRASSINGTON   (North-western extremity of the parish)

Mining. Lead mining remains are comparatively slight in this part of the parish.

Communications. The route of the Derby–Buxton Roman road is followed in this area by the parish's western boundary (see p 160).

BROUGH & SHATTON

Smelting. Lead smelting was carried on through the second half of

M

the nineteenth century and into the twentieth at the Brough White Lead Works (SK 182825), now the steel finishing works of Messrs Cooke & Stevenson (see p 52, and under 'Mills' below).

Mills. Brough Corn Mill (SK 183826), on its ancient site beside the River Noe, was rebuilt in 1924 following a fire in the previous year which destroyed an earlier building. Threshing was carried on at the mill and the grain dried in a kiln with grates and fires beneath before grinding. There were five sets of grindstones in the mill, worked by two waterwheels. One of the waterwheels, 12ft diameter and 6ft wide, still remains, although its wooden buckets are rotting. Electricity was generated until around 1950 when abstraction schemes to augment the Labybower Reservoir reduced the flow of water (see p 135). The building is now used mainly as a warehouse by Messrs William Eyre & Sons.

There were formerly three cotton mills at Brough. One was the later Brough White Lead Works (SK 182825), already mentioned above, of which buildings still remain. Another was near Brough House, and now comprises cottages (SK 180824). The third was Stretfield or Brough New Mill (SK 178820); this was owned by Thomas Somerset until the business failed towards the end of the nineteenth century, reputedly because of the high cost of new machinery. The premises were subsequently in the hands of various owners and used for wire manufacture, for the making of combs from ox horn, as a cement workers' hostel, and for other purposes; they are now empty.

Agriculture. Sheep were formerly washed in the Overdale Brook on Shatton Moor, and also in Shatton village.

BRUSHFIELD

Mining. There are considerable remains of lead mining. Still remembered locally is the frequency of horses' deaths from bellanding and the consequent relief to farmers when tractors came into use.

Communications. Part of the disused Midland Railway line, including the 515yd long Litton Tunnel is in the north of the parish.

BUBNELL—see BASLOW & BUBNELL

BUTTERTON

Pinfold. There was formerly a pinfold in the village, between the church and the chapel (SK 075566), now a private garden.

Communications. The road on the route of the former Leek & Manifold Valley Light Railway, including the brick-lined Swainsley Tunnel (154yd long, 12ft 9in wide, 15ft 3in high), skirts the parish's eastern boundary (see p 179).

CALVER

Mining. There are considerable remains of lead working, particularly in the west and south of the parish.

The situation of Calver Sough, the former engine house and chimney stack at SK 239747, and the Brightside and Red Rake sough tails at SK 242745 and SK 239741 respectively are described on pp 46–7. Site of former ore-dressing floor at SK 239741.

Quarrying. The limestone quarry (SK 237746) at which limekilns also operated, ceased being worked around 1900.

Mills, etc. The former Calver Corn Mill (SK 244744) was built on the present site when ousted from its previous position through the building of Calver Cotton Mill. Though milling has long ceased the building remains; the area of the mill pond has been drained. A smelting mill may have occupied this site in earlier days.

Calver Mill (SK 247745), formerly for cotton and now used for the manufacture of stainless steel sinks, is described on pp 110–12.

The bootmaking business of Messrs Heginbotham was started around 1918 as an expansion of the industry at Stoney Middleton.

Pinfold. There are no remains of the pinfold which was situated in the village just above the cross at SK 240746.

CASTLETON

Mining. There are considerable remains of lead mining. In the north of the parish lie the Odin (SK 135834), Treak Cliff (SK 136832), Blue John (SK 132832), Old Tor (SK 135827) and Speedwell (SK 139827) Mines (see pp 23, 44, 52, 55) and in the south the workings on Oxlow and Dirtlow Rakes (see pp 43–4).

Quarrying. Limestone workings include Windy Knoll Quarry (SK 126830).

Mills, etc. The former Castleton Corn Mill (SK 151831) was used for grinding until the 1920s. Subsequently the 400-year-old limestone building was used as an antique store and then by the High Peak Mining & Engineering Company. Since 1962 the premises have been adapted and used by Cambrian Electronics Products Ltd but with preservation of certain mill features including the wheelpit which is now the canteen and displays a portion of original walling. The former oak waterwheel of 10–12ft diameter was broken up in the 1950s but the leat supplied by the Peakshole Water and the mill pond can still be seen.

Immediately north of the old corn mill is another building, about 300 years old, which was formerly a sawmill.

There were formerly two cotton spinning mills at Castleton, one of them, at least, possibly situated on Goosehill (see p 104).

Opposite the school, at SK 150829, is a former chapel which from 1898 to the 1930s housed a mineral water factory, and was later used as a furniture store.

The ropewalk in Peak Cavern (SK 148826) is described on p 121.

Agriculture. Enclosure walls displaying S-shaped curves can be seen to the east of the village (see p 139).

There are remains of a circular pinfold in a field south of the road from Pindale (SK 153826).

CHAPEL-EN-LE-FRITH   (The south-west and north-east portions only)

Mining. There are remains of lead mining in the eastern section, including Coalpithole Mine (SK 092813) and shafts farther east.

Quarrying. There are various old quarries and gravel pits.

Mills, etc. The site of the former corn mill at Combs (SK 045782) is marked by some wall remains and the mill dam. The mill house is below.

Brook House Farm, Combs (SK 043784) was once a brewery and a building adjoining may have been used for cotton manufacture or for bootmaking.

Rye Flatt (SK 045781) was the 'birthplace of Ferodo' (the brake-lining manufacturing firm). Herbert Frood, a former boot salesman, came here at the end of the nineteenth century and experimented in his production of brake linings. The use by farmers of old boots to aid worn-out braking blocks on carts gave him the idea; he worked in a shed in the garden of Rye Flatt and with power from a waterwheel produced a 'brake shoe' made from belting impregnated with a bitu-minous solution, using lanes in the surrounding hills as testing ground. Frood shortly moved his business into the town of Chapel-en-le-Frith where today the modern manufacture is a large and important industry.

Near Lower Plumpton (SK 073798) is the site of a former barytes works, latterly used as a laundry.

Agriculture. There was a sheepwash on the Pyegreave Brook.

CHARLESWORTH   (All of the parish except the extreme west)

Quarrying. There are numerous millstone grit quarries at some of which stone was ground for sand; the quarry at Sandmill Hollow, south of Chunal, where this was done, and the discarded crushing stone (SK 033905) are mentioned on p 83. For the Glossop Low

Quarries (SK 058961), worked for paving stones and slates and closed since the end of the nineteenth century, see p 88.

Mills. The former Gnathole Woollen Mill (SK 039924) is now a farmhouse and flats (see p 102). Many workers lived at nearby Chunal where in the nineteenth century there were numerous cottages in addition to a cotton mill and a dye house.

At Fair Vage Clough (SK 079990) are the ruins of a former paper mill, see p 97.

Water. The southern sections of the Woodhead (SK 090995), Torside (SK 065985), Rhodeswood (SK 050982), Vale House (SK 038976) and Bottoms (SK 028969) Reservoirs lie within the parish, also the smaller Hurst (SK 056937), Mossylee (SK 057946) and Swineshaw (SK 043957), (see pp 129–30).

Agriculture. At the time of the 'cotton panic' in the mid-nineteenth century the Duke of Norfolk found work for many people in the Glossop area in the digging and laying of stone drains on hill land. Examples are seen at Mossylee (SK 063946) draining to the Yellowslacks Brook. About 60 acres here were dug by hand, drained, fenced and reseeded on the western slopes of Shelf Moor. The drains are of about a shovel's width, the minor ones are open—though now to a large extent fallen in—but some of the main drains are of the stone box type and still moderately effective.

There are the remains of a sheepwash on the Shelf Brook (SK 062943) with pens still partially left standing.

Communications. The route of the Doctor's Gate Roman road passes through the parish near the Shelf Brook and Mossylee (see p 159).

Woodhead railway station was closed for goods on 1 July 1963 and for passengers on 27 July 1964; Crowden station closed for both goods and passengers on 4 February 1957.

CHELMORTON

Mining. There are remains of lead mining, particularly north of the village.

Quarrying. Numerous small quarry workings used as sources of stone for the considerable amount of limestone walling in the parish include one in Horseshoe Dale (SK 098697) from which roadmaking material was also extracted. There were formerly also many small limekilns, fired by coal from the workings on Axe Edge.

Agriculture. Some explanation for the intensive system of stone-walled enclosures close to the village is given on p 139.

The former pinfold is still intact, on the east side of the village street opposite the lower of two butcher's shops; it is irregularly triangular in shape with the highest of its walls nearest the road.

CHINLEY, BUXWORTH & BROWNSIDE (Northern and eastern sections only)

Smelting. The name Bole Hill (SK 050839) suggests a site where smelting was done.

Quarrying. For the Cracken Edge Quarry, on the eastern slopes of Chinley Churn (SK 037836) see p 88.

Chinley Head Quarry (SK 050844) was formerly worked for the production of dressed building stone.

COLNE VALLEY (Southern section only)

The moorland area is almost entirely gathering ground for the Wessenden Head (SE 070075), Wessenden Old (SE 060085), Blakeley (SE 054095) and Butterly (SE 050103) Reservoirs, see p 132.

The Redbrook (SE 027098), Swellands (SE 037090) and Black Moss (SE 032087) Reservoirs were constructed as feeders for the Huddersfield Canal, which they still supply.

COMBS—see CHAPEL-EN-LE-FRITH

CRESSBROOK—see LITTON

CURBAR

Quarrying. There are remains of quarrying and millstone working along Curbar Edge.

Mill. Ruins beside the Barbrook (SK 275739) are of an old corn mill, disused for many years; it is believed that there was previously a lead smelting mill on the site. The former mill pond is still marked by a rushy area which often holds water and a wooden balk forming a weir is still in position upstream. A stone bridge gives access across the stream from the direction of the A621 road.

Pinfold. The former pinfold is situated beside the road at the bottom of Pinfold Hill (SK 250746). It is circular, with high walls.

DERWENT

Quarrying. There are numerous old quarries previously worked for millstone grit including one north of the A57 road at Ladybower (SK 209868).

Mill. The name Mill Brook indicates the existence of an earlier mill, but none is known in living memory.

Water. The village of Derwent was drowned by construction of the Ladybower Reservoir (see p 135).

Communications. The rebuilt ancient packhorse bridge across the Derwent, removed in 1942 during construction of the Ladybower Reservoir, can be seen at Slippery Stones (SK 168951).

DUNFORD   (Western section only)

Quarrying. There are a number of disused millstone grit quarries including the extensive Magnum Quarries (SE 145042). These were worked largely for building stone but have been disused since the 1920s and the surrounding area, which formerly contained many workers' habitations, has become mainly depopulated. Other quarries were those at Winscar (SE 153034) which were worked up to World War I.

Water. The parish contains the Snailsden (SE 133039), Harden (SE 150036), Dunford Bridge (SE 150026), Lower Windleden (SE 156017) and Upper Windleden (SE 152012) Reservoirs (see p 133).

Communications. There is a former toll bar cottage at Dunford Bridge (SE 157024).

Part of the Woodhead Tunnel and its eastern portal are in the parish (see pp 171–4). The goods station at Dunford Bridge was a busy coal-handling depot until its closure on 16 December 1963.

EARL STERNDALE—see HARTINGTON MIDDLE QUARTER

EATON & ALSOP

Quarrying. There were formerly numerous small quarry workings and up to later years the large limestone quarry at SK 163566. Work started here in about 1870 when Messrs Hall & Boardman used kilns for brickmaking, extracting sand for the purpose from an open pit; this pit, containing water, can still be seen (SK 160565). Later, limestone burning was done and eventually the quarry was taken over and worked extensively by ICI, with operation of a Hoffman kiln. Working ceased in 1959, since when the kilns have been demolished and the area of the quarry levelled and grassed.

Agriculture. Examples of lynchets can be seen on the hillside of Crosslow, to the north of Alsop village.

Communications. The disused track of the former L & NW railway from Ashbourne to Buxton runs through the parish. There were formerly sidings to the south of the A515 road which served the Alsop Quarry.

ECTON—see WETTON

EDALE

Quarrying. A millstone grit quarry on Nether Tor (SK 123876) was formerly worked for local use; the church and other buildings in the village are constructed of its stone.

Mills. The disused Edale Cotton Mill (SK 134854) is described on p 113 (also see plate, p 90).

Skinners Hall (SK 129853) was formerly a hostel for workers at the tannery which preceded the cotton mill.

Agriculture. 'Booth' occurring in place names (eg Grindsbrook Booth, Ollerbrook Booth, Nether Booth) is a survival of earlier days when a booth was a temporary home or shed for cowherds or booth-men in charge of stock in the forest area. Eventually they became permanent homesteads and even hamlets.

There was a sheepwash below Nether Tor (SK 119870) with folds still remaining, last used around 1930. Sheepwashing was also done at Upper Booth and Barber Booth.

Communications. Edale was important on packhorse routes; note-worthy are the packhorse bridge at SK 088862 near Jacob's Ladder, on the way to Edale Cross and Hayfield, and the name Jaggers Clough (SK 144877).

Considerable mounds in the valley near Barber Booth, known locally as 'the tips', consist of spoil from the construction of the Cowburn Tunnel.

Edale station was closed for goods traffic on 7 October 1963.

EDENSOR

Mill. The shell of an old corn mill, built in the mid-eighteenth century in typical Chatsworth style, stands beside the River Derwent (SK 259688). From the weir across the river the head race, formerly controlled by a sluice, runs underground for a stretch and then in the open; the tail race discharges back into the river through a stone-

18.9.70

Removal of Evam's industrial landmark

NEWS of the impending demolition of Glebe Mine's former laboratory premises was reported to Evam Parish Council and will result in the removal of an industrial landmark.

This is the former shoe factory of E. West and Sons Ltd., which gave employment to a considerable number of operatives and at one time made a salutary contribution to the export market. Before its conversion into a slipper factory, the older part of the building served as the village school which closed about 80 years ago. The school had a wooden gallery and a strip of garden skirting the road was used as an extension of the factory premises. A red brick chimney was another feature of the factory when machinery was driven by steam power.

Miss Edith Ethel Hart, 3 Balmoak Lane, Tapton, Chesterfield, who died on June 17 last, left £14,895 gross, £14,784 net. Duty £1,201. Probate has been granted to her sister Miss Constance N. Hart, 21 Taylor Court, Tilehurst Road, Reading, and John Blakesley, solicitor, of Chesterfield.

Mr. Ernest Edward Henson, 89 Blacksmith Lane, Calow, Chesterfield, who died on June 5 last, intestate, left £2,848 gross, £2,743 net. Letters of Administration have been granted to his widow Mrs. Evelyn Henson.

Mr. Edward Sidney Morris, 47 York Street, Hasland, Chesterfield, who died on June 26 last, intestate, left £2,863 gross, £2,773 net. Letters of administration have been granted to his son Duncan E. Morris, of 40 Smithfield Avenue, Hasland.

Mrs. Violet Jane Newton, 12 North Road, Clowne, who died on March 1 last, intestate, wife of Richard Newton, ironmonger, left £7,283 gross, £7,220 net. Letters of Administration have been granted to her husband.

walled arched culvert. Part of the large undershot waterwheel remains as well as some of the internal machinery, and a millstone (convex on one side) rests against an outer wall. The mill was last worked by Mr Wilfrid Johnson (previously by a George Hodkin) for grinding corn up to 1950. Damage was caused in about 1962 when trees were blown on to the mill during a gale.

ELKSTONE—see WARSLOW & ELKSTONES

ELTON

Mining. There are considerable remains of lead mining in the southern (limestone) part of the parish.

Quarrying. Bury Cliff Quarry (SK 217616), disused for many years, was formerly worked for grindstones and building stone. Pulping stones were supplied from the quarry to Scandinavia for paper-making.

Watts Cliff Quarry (SK 221621) is still in use. A very fine 'lilac' coloured gritstone is extracted and used for building work, for fireplaces and for grindstones exported to the USA, Ghana and other countries.

Pinfold. The site of the former pinfold is by the green (SK 218609).

EYAM

Mining. There are considerable remains of lead mining throughout the parish in the form of grass-covered mounds and shafts. Glebe Mine, in the village (SK 219764), has in recent times been used for fluorspar extraction and is connected underground with Ladywash Mine (SK 218775), through which veins in the limestone underlying Hucklow Edge are currently worked for fluorspar by Laporte Industries Ltd (see p 56). The square chimney and engine house of New Engine Mine (SK 224774), still in reasonable condition, form a prominent landmark; here was the deepest lead mineshaft in Derbyshire, reaching 1,092ft in about 1860 and last worked in 1884. Shaw Engine Mine (SK 222771), Brookhead Mine (SK 221768) and Black Engine Mine (SK 197778) are all marked by hillocks.

During the early years of the present century a light narrow-gauge railway was built for carrying fluorspar material from hillocks along the Edgeside vein to a loading point opposite Waterfall Farm (SK 199770) from where haulage continued by road to Grindleford station. During World War I a locomotive called 'The Spar Queen' provided the motive power on the rails; afterwards, steam wagons were in use.

Quarrying. There are large limestone quarries south of the village, alongside the A623 road and in Eyam Dale, which were much worked in the past. Lime was burnt in huge kilns. Rate-payers still enjoy the right to take stone for their use from certain 'town quarries'. Gritstone quarries to the north were formerly worked for building purposes and for roofing and paving slabs but, since falling into disuse, these have been filled in with mining waste.

Mills, etc. There was formerly a windmill at SK 213766 (see p 95). Stone from its demolition was used for building a school but the original corn store still remains, together with one or two grinding stones. A garden covers the site.

Bradshaw Hall (SK 216767) was at one time used as a cotton factory. Silk weaving was also done in the village (see p 115); Ralph Wain's silk factory was at SK 213767, where the original mill and cottages below, bearing the date 1733 and now enlarged, are used for shoe manufacture by Messrs G. Robinson & Company Ltd.

There was at one time a mineral water factory at the road junction at SK 216768, but long since demolished.

EYAM WOODLANDS

Quarrying. Millstone grit for local use has been worked in a small quarry at SK 234778, and also in a quarry beside the A622 road (SK 240794), which was reputedly also worked for grindstones.

Tanning. Grindleford Model Laundry uses premises of a former tannery (SK 243773). The laundry has been in existence since 1913 and the tannery operated previously. Cottages at the roadside were built with stone from some of the tannery's demolished buildings.

Pinfold. There is a former pinfold at the foot of the Sir William Hill (SK 242778).

FAWFIELDHEAD

Quarrying. In addition to minor quarrying remains there are also various limekilns; one, almost hidden by weed, is by the Blake Brook ford south of Ludburn (SK 092621).

Clay was worked on Reaps Moor and bricks manufactured in a field now marked by deep undulations (SK 085619). Believed to have been started by an industrialist from the Potteries, the industry employed inmates of a workhouse which existed in the parish. It ended in about 1860.

Mill. The site of Ludburn Corn Mill is marked by a depression in a field by the Blake Brook, and the mill dam by a patch of rushes (SK 094620).

Agriculture. Sheep were washed in the Blake Brook, by the ford (SK 092621). There was formerly a pool at this point and further depth was effected by partial damming of the stream.

Cheese factory. The Reapsmoor cheese factory (SK 087619) is described on p 154 (also see plate, p 126).

Communications. The northern terminus of the Leek & Manifold Valley Light Railway was at Hulme End (SK 102593).

FENNY BENTLEY

Communications. The disused track of the former L & NW Railway from Ashbourne to Buxton, now the 'Tissington Trail' runs through the parish. The Fenny Bentley goods depot was closed to rail traffic on 7 October 1963.

(In past days many people living in Fenny Bentley worked at the nearby Woodeaves Cotton Mill, see p 113.)

FLAGG

Mining. There are considerable remains of lead mining throughout the parish, including hillocks at SK 139698 which mark the site of Hubbadale Mine where rich deposits of lead were discovered in the eighteenth century.

Quarrying. There is much use of surface worked limestone, and in a field close to a minor road north-west of the village (SK 127696) is a good example of a small double limekiln (see plate, p 35).

Communications. Part of the route of the Derby–Buxton Roman road forms the parish boundary to the south-west (see p 160).

FLASH—see QUARNFORD

FOOLOW

Mining. There are considerable remains of lead mining. These include Watergrove Mine, immediately north of the A623 road (SK 188758), which was worked during the eighteenth century and until 1853; water was a constant problem here, necessitating soughs and pumping engines, and an 80ft high square chimney built for a Fairbairn beam engine in 1837 was a prominent landmark until its demolition in 1960. Water from the disused mine is currently pumped and piped to the Cavendish Mill of Laporte Industries Ltd at Stoney Middleton.

Farther north in the parish are the remains of Slaters Engine Mine (SK 192778) and of Bradshaw Mine (SK 196778), both marked by hillocks.

FROGGATT

Smelting. Tumbled ruins at SK 247771 in Hay Wood are probably remains of an eighteenth-century slag mill. These consist of partial walls of a small building measuring 10ft 6in × 6ft 4in internally with walls 1ft 9in thick. There is a 1ft 6in wide opening in the front wall and in the one opposite a recess 2ft 6in wide, 5ft 4in high with a sloping back, evidently where the waterwheel was accommodated. At the higher level, water from a stream is diverted through open-ended stone troughs forming a launder, to fall into the ruined chamber. The gritstone sections of the launder are from 2ft 9in to 3ft 11in in length and have a square channel roughly 9in wide and 9in deep, with an overall width of 1ft 8in. Smelting is believed to have been done here.

Quarrying. There are remains of millstone quarrying on Froggatt Edge.

At Top of the Hay (SK 248769) are remains of a limekiln. It is said that in the nineteenth century men used to bring coal here from Holmesfield before proceeding to the limestone quarry at Calver and that for carting two loads of limestone from the quarry up to the kiln they were allowed a load of burnt lime for the price of 6d (2½p).

Communications. A track along Froggatt Edge marks the former old road from Baslow to Sheffield.

GLOSSOP—see CHARLESWORTH

GRANGE MILL—see IVONBROOK GRANGE; IBLE

GRATTON

Agriculture. Sheep were washed in the stream at SK 209617, where there was a ford.

Cheese factory. A stone building beside the road at SK 209616, now used for poultry, was formerly a cheese factory (see p 155).

GREAT HUCKLOW

Mining. This was a busy lead-mining village up to the end of the nineteenth century. Pits, dumps and buildings near the village, at SK 177780, are remains of the Mill Dam Mine; the former office is now a dwelling house, the blacksmith's shop still stands and what is now the theatre is believed to have been formerly used for smelting. Until about 1890 there were two tall chimneys in the village, one by the public house and another close to the present theatre.

Mounds and shafts west, north and east of the village mark the sites of other smaller mines on the Hucklow vein.

Pinfold. There is said to have been a pinfold on the road from the village to the school.

GREAT LONGSTONE

Mining. There are considerable lead-mining remains in the northern part of the parish including those of Deep Rake, traditionally worked by the Romans, and others on Longstone Edge, though to a large extent disturbed due to more recent working for fluorspar.

Quarrying. Various quarrying remains include former chert pits.

Pinfold. There was formerly a pinfold at the bottom of Church Lane, on the site of the present Institute.

Communications. The disused Midland Railway line passes through the extreme south of the parish. Great Longstone passenger station (SK 197710) was officially closed on 10 September 1962.

GREEN FAIRFIELD   (South-west tip of the parish)

Water. A turbine powered by the River Wye at SK 093725 operates a pump which raises spring water to Pictor Hall and farms above.

GRINDLEFORD—see EYAM WOODLANDS; NETHER PADLEY

GRINDLOW

Mining. There are remains of lead mining, particularly in the north below Hucklow Edge, including those of Silence Mine (SK 188780) which closed in 1885. Excess water is said to have been a main problem here.

GRINDON

Mining. Some fenced shafts mark an area of old lead mines on the north side of Ossom's Hill (SK 092559). There is another shaft at Coxengreen (SK 074562).

Quarrying. There are remains of quarrying on Grindon Moor and south of Deepdale. Redmoorlane Quarry (SK 093541) was worked by local people and stone broken by hand as late as 1932, during time of unemployment. Until recently a limekiln remained here.

Mill. Ford Mill (SK 067534), a former corn mill, has been in disuse since about 1900. The buildings are now used for agricultural purposes but the massive wooden mechanism still remains within, at least in 1969. The former wheelpit has been roofed over as part of the building but the course of the leat bringing water from the River Hamps, and of the millpond, is clearly traceable.

Pinfold. A stone post and a section of the circular pinfold wall remain in the village, opposite the inn (SK 086543).

Communications. The footpath on the route of the former Leek & Manifold Valley Light Railway follows closely the Rivers Hamps and Manifold on the parish's eastern boundary (see p 179).

HARTHILL

Mining and Smelting. The northern area of the parish was extensively worked for lead, unwatered by various soughs (including the Hillcarr) and by hydraulic and steam engines (see pp 39, 45). Surface remains consist of hillocks and numerous shafts; these include Greenfield shaft (SK 224635), now partially covered with stones, which was reached by the Hillcarr Sough in 1783. Half a mile to the north, cottages at Broadmeadow (SK 224643) were the offices of the Alport

N

Mining Company; near them is Broadmeadow shaft, formerly served by two hydraulic engines. The site of Brown Bank ventilation shaft on the Hillcarr Sough is marked by a mound west of the A524 road (SK 231630).

For the cupola of the Alport Smelting Works (SK 223648), see p 51.

Quarrying. Quarrying remains include former limestone workings behind Alport Mill (SK 222646), with two limekilns, used until the time of World War I.

Mill. Alport Corn Mill on the River Lathkill (SK 223646) is of ancient origin. There is known to have been a corn mill at Alport in the twelfth century, undoubtedly on the same site. Owned by the Duke of Rutland and leased to Messrs Johnson, Alport Mill was last worked properly in about 1925; it is now used as a store for corn and feeding stuffs. A portion of the older building has been removed and some additions made. The breast-type waterwheel, approximately 4ft wide, with iron buckets, is still in position and inside the mill are five pairs of millstones (plate, p 71).

Pinfold. Some remains of a squarish pinfold can be seen by the crossroads at SK 223643.

Communications. Alport was a point on the ancient Port Way. There is a packhorse bridge at Bradford (SK 215641) and another at Alport (SK 222645).

HARTINGTON MIDDLE QUARTER

Mining. There are remains of old mines at the top of Dowel Dale, also south of Brierlow and around Earl Sterndale.

Quarrying. Remains of limestone quarrying can be seen at the top of Dowel Dale and around Earl Sterndale, with a large limekiln at SK 089674. A once familiar roadside limekiln beside a disused quarry on the hill east of Crowdecote (SK 106650) apparently collapsed during the winter of 1969–70 (plate, p 36).

Pits at Blake Moor (SK 158629) were formerly worked for pocket silicas.

Cheese factory. The former Glutton cheese factory (SK 084666) is now used as a garage (see p 155).

Communications. A section of the A515 road, from SK 128665 to SK 117676, follows the line of the former Derby–Buxton Roman road (see p 160).

A packhorse route crossed the Dove at Crowdecote and the Packhorse Inn was reputedly a stopping point with stabling facilities.

A section of the former Cromford & High Peak Railway, later part of the L & NWR, runs through the parish and includes part of the Newhaven Tunnel (SK 151629). At Hurdlow the course of the earlier C & HP route, abandoned from 2 January 1869, can be seen leading off to the Hurdlow incline on the west, marked by a line of electric pylons (see pp 168–71). Hurdlow station (SK 127660) was closed for both passenger and goods traffic on 15 August 1949. The first Parsley Hay station (SK 146635) closed for passengers on 4 August 1899 and for goods on 6 July 1964; the second, passenger, station closed on 1 November 1954.

HARTINGTON NETHER QUARTER

Mining. There are numerous minor signs of lead mining. Ironstone is said to have been worked in Friden Hollow.

Quarrying. There are various disused limestone quarries. These include the Hartshead Quarry near Heathcote (SK 149607), used during World War II for supplying stone for making aerodrome runways, and the rather older Hartington Station Quarry (SK 151612). There is a large limekiln at SK 143607, beside the road to Hartington village, near an old quarry.

For the silica works at Friden and its associated system of tramways see pp 78–81.

Agriculture. There is a circular pinfold beside the road running due south from Biggin, in good condition although its former arched doorway is now gone (SK 155593). There is said to have been another pinfold at Newhaven.

Sheep were washed in places in the River Dove.

There is an ancient mere near Heathcote (SK 143602) and a well nearby.

Communications. The route of the Derby–Buxton Roman road forms the parish boundary on the east.

Newhaven was a changing post on the old Manchester–London coach route.

The track of the disused Cromford & High Peak Railway passes through the eastern part of the parish; Friden station formerly served the Derbyshire Silica Firebrick works' private siding until closure on 2 October 1967 (SK 172607).

The disused track of the former L & NW railway from Ashbourne to Buxton, now the 'Tissington Trail', runs through the western part of the parish (see pp 175–6). Hartington station (SK 149611) closed to passenger traffic on 1 November 1954 and for goods on 6 July 1964.

HARTINGTON TOWN QUARTER

Mining. There are minor remains of lead mining, chiefly in the north.

Quarrying. There are silica workings in the north. At SK 145628 are the remains of the High Peak Silica Works, comprising a long low building and two square chimney stacks, with traces of the narrow-gauge inclined plane which was used for raising material from the pits. Firebricks were made here during the lifetime of the Ashbourne–Buxton railway, to which the works were aligned, until the 1950s. More recently other firms have extracted the silica sand for use in glassmaking.

Mills. Hartington Corn Mill (SK 120598) said to date back 400 or 500 years, is now converted to a dwelling house and the undershot waterwheel, 13ft diameter, 6ft wide, iron-framed and with wooden buckets, is preserved. Water continues to flow through the recon-ditioned leat in the garden from the weir on the River Dove. The mill was latterly worked by Messrs Caudwell; it was used during World War II for grinding farmers' oats and later for storage.

Farther upstream on the Dove was Ludwell Corn Mill (SK 124623), long since incorporated into farm buildings. The dam is still visible.

Pinfold. About half of a circular pinfold still remains by the road east of the village (SK 132605), now incorporated into a council depot.

Cheese factory. The Hartington Cheese Factory (SK 126604), west of the village, is still in use for the manufacture of Stiltons (see p 153).

Communications. The disused track of the former L & NW railway from Ashbourne to Buxton runs through the western part of the parish, which also contains part of the Newhaven Tunnel of the C & HP (SK 151629).

HARTINGTON UPPER QUARTER   (All of the parish except a section south and east of Buxton)

Mining. There are some remains of lead mining in the limestone area to the south.

Signs of former coal working can still be seen on Goyt's Moss and at Dane Head on Axe Edge Moor. Errwood House also had its own private coal mines, one near the house and one in Shooters Clough (see pp 92–3).

Quarrying. There are a number of old limestone quarries in the south.

Gritstone workings in the north of the parish include the Goytsclough Quarry (SK 011734), see pp 88, 163.

Mills. At SK 012733, near the quarry, is the site of the former Goytsclough Mill, used for making paint. Water was taken by leat from the Goyt and also from a stream in Deep Clough and held in a dam for powering the waterwheel. There were formerly also cottages here for employees.

Remains of the Fernilee Gunpowder Mill are submerged beneath the Fernilee Reservoir at SK 013771 (see pp 100–1).

Agriculture. Washgate on the River Dove (SK 053673), with stone pens, was one place where sheep were washed.

Communications. The route of the former Roman road from Buxton to Manchester can be seen continuing straight on where the present main road leaves it for the Long Hill (see p 160).

The present road and the earlier Long Hill route converge at SK 032752 and 026758 (see p 166).

There are packhorse bridges near Hopping, on the Hollinsclough–Booth road (SK 063669) and at Washgate (SK 053673) and one reconstructed in the Goyt Valley at SK 013732 (see p 162).

The route of the former Cromford & High Peak Railway runs through the parish. The section in the part of the parish north of Buxton, disused since 1892, includes the Burbage Tunnel (SK 031740) and the Bunsall incline at SK 021753 (see pp 167–71).

HASSOP

Mining. There are remains of lead mining in the north of the parish.

Quarrying. Cracknowl Quarry (SK 214704) was formerly worked for roadstone.

Pinfold. Remains of the pinfold, including a blocked-up entrance in the stone wall, can be seen on the north side of the Great Longstone road (SK 220722).

Communications. The disused Midland Railway line passes through the parish; Hassop station (SK 217705), now an agricultural machinery depot, was closed for passengers on 17 August 1942 and for goods on 5 October 1964.

HATHERSAGE   (See also SHEFFIELD)

Smelting. The name Bole Hill in the south of the parish is suggestive of early smelting. North-east of the village is the site of the Callow Bank Cupola (SK 252822), see p 51.

Quarrying. Workings for millstone grit include a quarry below Owler Tor (SK 256799) which was in use in 1811 and probably until the mid-nineteenth century; near it are remains of millstones in varying stages of completion. The disused Yarncliffe Quarry (SK 255794), bought by Sheffield Corporation in 1927, was in the past much worked for building stone. For the Bole Hill Quarries (SK 249795) from which the stone for the Howden and Derwent dams was extracted and the inclined plane at SK 246790 see p 91.

Mills, etc. Padley Mill (SK 250788), on the Burbage Brook, was originally a corn mill and latterly a sawmill at the time the Totley Tunnel was built. It is now a dwelling house; the mill pool and site of the waterwheel are still visible.

Leadmill (SK 233807), beside the River Derwent, is now a private residence. It may at some time have had a purpose connected with lead, but is known to have formerly been a corn mill, and latterly a stonemason's yard using water power for sawing and dressing stone; the leat is still visible.

Wire-drawing and the making of needles and pins were formerly important in Hathersage. For the four main centres: The Barnfield Works (SK 229814 and 228812); the former works of Messrs Cocker & Sons (SK 229814); Dale Mill (SK 235817); and another at the top of the main street (SK 233816) see pp 119–20.

Pinfold. The preserved pinfold can be seen beside Church Bank at SK 234818 (see p 142).

Communications. Hathersage station was closed for goods traffic on 30 January 1965.

HAYFIELD   (Excluding the village and its immediately surrounding area)

Smelting. There is a tradition of iron smelting in the distant past in a furnace in William Clough in the area now submerged by Stockport & District Water Board's reservoir, near the confluence of the Kinder and William Clough Brooks. Large mounds of slag were submerged beneath the water and further remains have been found upstream. The industry is said to have been the cause of original forest clearance in this area in the obtaining of wood for charcoal for the forge.

Quarrying. There are various gritstone quarries, used in the past for building stone and for millstone cutting. At Cluther Rocks (SK 073877), on the western slopes of Kinder Scout, there are the remains of a millstone quarry.

Mills. Both wool and cotton manufacturing have been of importance at Hayfield. There was formerly a fulling mill near The Ashes, on the Kinder slopes, and a wool spinning, weaving and cloth dressing mill at Phoside (SK 037859), see p 103.

The Primrose Vale Mills (SK 032879) were at one time a tannery, and also a buckram factory. The mill building, which stood beside the stream, is now completely removed, but still remaining is the old flue and, on the hillside above, the chimney stack. Workers' cottages here are said to have been built in about 1860.

For Clough Mill (SK 032882) at Little Hayfield, formerly used for cotton, see p 114.

The Bank Vale Paper Mill (SK 031875), dating from the early nineteenth century, now modernised, continues in operation under Messrs John Slack Ltd.

Agriculture. A sheepwash beside the River Kinder near Booth (SK 051876) which, with its accompanying sheep pens, can still be seen, was constructed at about the time of the building of the Kinder Reservoir in 1912, when development of the water supply prohibited the use of a wash at William Clough, farther upstream. The Booth sheepwash was last used in the early 1930s. There was another sheepwash at the foot of Oaken Clough, near Southhead Farm, where there are still remains of pens, and a further one in Hollingworth Clough (SK 035894).

Communications. Hayfield was important on packhorse routes (see p 163). There is a packhorse bridge, minus its parapets, just off the Kinder road (SK 050870).

HAZLEBADGE

Mining. There is considerable evidence throughout the parish of ground disturbance due to lead mining.

HEATHYLEE

Mills. For Longnor Mill on the River Manifold (SK 085646) see p 99. Dane's or Dean's Mill, which stood on a tributary of the River Churnet at Upper Hulme (SK 012613), is now demolished. Thos Hind was miller here in 1851.

Agriculture. Sheep were washed in the Oakenclough Brook near Hardings Booth.

HEATON (The north-eastern section of the parish)

Quarrying. Workings include the Shawbank Quarry (SJ 966626) and Gunstone Pits (SJ 965615).

Mills. Bearda Mill (SJ 963641), a former corn mill, is now a dwelling house. The waterwheel was removed long ago.

Just south of the latter, at SJ 964640, are the ruins of a sawmill (see p 98).

At SJ 963651 are the ruins of the Dane Bridge Silk Mill and the apparent area of the mill dam (see p 117).

HIGHLOW

Mill. At SK 214795, in the valley of the Bretton Brook, on the north side of the stream, is the site of an old corn mill, now almost completely indiscernible. The course of the leat can be traced, also the rush-growing depression of the mill pond. Pieces of stone walling with metal attachments, covered with lime trees, can be discovered in a corner of the field. Abraham Walker was the miller here in 1857 but the mill was in disuse within a few years of that date.

HOLLINSCLOUGH

Quarrying. There are a number of minor quarries, worked in the past simply for local use.

Silk. Silk weaving was formerly a cottage industry in Hollinsclough (see p 115).

Agriculture. Sheep were formerly washed in the River Dove near Stannery.

Communications. There are packhorse bridges near Hopping, on the Hollinsclough–Booth bridle road (SK 063669) and at Washgate (SK 053673).

HOLMESFIELD   (The western section of the parish)

Smelting. The name Bole Hill (SK 295747) suggests a place where smelting was done.

HOLMFIRTH   (Holme Ward only)

Quarrying. There are a number of disused gritstone quarry workings.

Mills. The village of Holme was formerly much involved with the woollen industry. Former weaving sheds, since converted to cottages, stand by the roadside at SE 103056 (see p 102 and plate, p 72). Part of a large house in the village (SE 108059) was formerly a warehouse. Details of woollen mills which formerly existed in the vicinity, and of the holes for tenterhooks seen in a roadside wall (SE 109061) are given on p 103 and see plate, p 72. (See also pp 130–2 for an account of mills flooded by reservoirs.)

Water. Holme Ward contains the Bilberry Reservoir (SE 102070) and the Digley (SE 108070) as well as the Yateholme (SE 111046), Riding Wood (SE 116050) and Ramsden (SE 114054), see pp 130–3.

Pinfold. A former pinfold in the centre of the village was obliterated only in recent years.

Communications. Holme was well situated on the packhorse routes connecting with Derbyshire, with an interchange of lime and woollen goods (see p 163).

HOPE

Mining and Smelting. Pindale or Ashton's Mine (SK 162826), sunk through overlying shale into the northern extremity of Dirtlow Rake, was being worked for lead in the early nineteenth century. Besides old mining dumps the engine house and square chimney still survive at Pindale Farm.

There are remains of a former cupola amongst farm buildings at Marsh Farm (SK 163835), see p 52.

Quarrying. There are various small gritstone quarries including one on Hope Brink (SK 179849). In the south of the parish are clay pits and quarry workings and the large cement works of the Cement Marketing Company Ltd with its railway extension from the Hope Valley line.

Mills, etc. The former Hope Corn Mill (SK 174838) on the River Noe was in 1969 converted to a dwelling house after being disused for a number of years. The date 1866 on the main building probably indicates its renovation, or addition to an older building adjoining, undoubtedly the earlier mill. The letters JRC are believed to have been the initials of a John Robert Cocker of Hathersage. Threshing was done at the mill and the corn dried by coke fires before being ground. The building was also used as a sawmill, with a subsidiary wheel at the front taking power from the main waterwheel. The waterwheel, of about 11ft diameter and 3ft width, has been dismantled and removed, although reassembly is envisaged. While the wheelpit no longer exists and the leats and pond have been rendered at least temporarily dry, various mill features have been preserved and blended into the reconstruction.

Former cotton weaving sheds on the east side of the Edale road out of the village (SK 173835) can be identified by faintly visible blocked doorways.

Pinfold. The well-preserved Hope pinfold on the Pindale road (SK 172833) is described on pp 141–2.

Communications. The probable route of the Doctor's Gate Roman road runs northwards through the parish and over Hope Brink (see p 159).

HOPE WOODLANDS

Quarrying. There are various minor quarry workings for millstone grit.

Agriculture. The hills in this area are the home of the almost extinct Woodland White-faced breed of sheep (see p 149).

Before construction of the Ladybower dam, sheep were washed in the River Ashop upstream of the present reservoir.

Communications. The A57 road over the Snake Pass was one of the last great turnpikes, constructed 1818–21.

IBLE

Quarrying. A quarry at SK 253567 was worked for basalt until earlier this century (see p 77).

Mill. A corn mill at SK 246569, near the Lilies Inn, was in use until about 1900 but is now a ruin.

Agriculture. A sheepwash with pens beside the Via Gellia was used within living memory.

There are still remains of the irregularly shaped pinfold in the village (SK 249570). Parts of the walls remain, but not the door.

Cheese factory. The former Grange Mill Cheese Factory (SK 244576) was built in 1875 (see p 155).

ILAM

Mining. There are a few shaft remains of old lead mines scattered over the north of the parish, including Bincliff Mines (SK 117538) and Highfields Mine (SK 119536), also a miner's cottage at SK 135528.

Quarrying. Old limestone quarries on Ilam Tops were worked up to the 1930s.

Agriculture. Sheep were formerly washed in both the Rivers Dove and Manifold.

There is a small pinfold, roughly rectangular, at SK 133520 on the west side of the road to Wetton, opposite a small wood.

IVONBROOK GRANGE

Mining. There is evidence that the area of Shothouse Springs (SK 242589) (the site now occupied by the electricity station) was in medieval times a communal lead-ore washing place.

Mill. A building at SK 243577 was formerly a corn mill. Dating from at least as early as the eighteenth century, it has not been used in living memory and the waterwheel no longer exists.

KETTLESHULME

Mill. Lamb Hole or Lumb Mill (SJ 988804) was the site of a former cotton mill destroyed by fire in the 1820s. The shell of the burnt-out building was bought by a Mr Sheldon who reconstructed the present gritstone building in 1835 and adapted it for making candlewick for miners' lamps. The manufacture continued, providing the main source of local livelihood, until World War I when demand for candlewick declined. The premises were subsequently used for a time for making linen sheets. Originally lit by oil, the mill manufactured its own gas supply for lighting purposes until changing to water-generated electricity. The iron waterwheel inside the building, of 24ft diameter and 6ft width, has been undergoing restoration and the fitting of new buckets, and it is planned to use the wheel for generating electricity. Water from the Todd Brook, dammed above the waterfall, goes underground to a mill pond at the lower side of the building (plate, p 107).

KING STERNDALE

Communications. The parish has for many years been the home of the Pickford family (see p 163). It is reputed that the carriers' horses were changed here on the journeys to and from London and the men rested, and also that an enormous limekiln was built in the parish by a member of the family from which burnt limestone was distributed throughout Derbyshire.

LEA HALL

Part of the Woodeaves Mill dam is in the south of the parish.

LEEKFRITH (All of the parish except the extreme south)

Mining. Open shafts near Hazel Barrow, two encircled by stone walling and one by a wire fence (SK 009633 and 010633) visible from the nearby minor road, are the remains of coal mining up to the end of the nineteenth century.

Quarrying. The Roach Quarries (SK 003623), formerly a source of much millstone grit for building purposes, have long been disused.

Mills. A former corn mill at Meerbrook (SK 993607) was demolished prior to the area being flooded by the enlarging of the Tittesworth Reservoir in the early 1960s.

For the Upper Hulme Mill of Messrs William Tatton & Company (SK 012609) see p 118.

LITTLE HUCKLOW

Mining. There are considerable remains of lead mining, particularly in the south of the parish along High Rake. The Old Bulls Head Inn has an interesting collection of ore crushing stones, miners' picks and other local industrial relics.

Mills. The name of the hamlet Windmill suggests one having been there, but no traces are known. Certainly the situation would have been advantageous.

Pinfold. There was a pinfold in the village but its site is undisclosed.

LITTLE LONGSTONE

Mining. There are various scattered remains of lead mining.

Quarrying. Various sites of former limestone quarrying, particularly in the west.

Communications. The disused Midland Railway line runs through the parish and includes part of the 533yd long Headstone Tunnel and the Cressbrook Tunnel, 471yd in length. The River Wye is crossed by the spectacular Monsal Dale Viaduct; Monsal Dale station was closed on 10 August 1959.

LITTON

Mining. There are numerous scattered remains of lead mining.

Quarrying. In addition to various small limestone workings there is the disused basalt quarry in Tideswell Dale (SK 154738) now owned by the Peak Park Planning Board and adapted as a picnic site (see p 77).

Mills. For Litton Mill on the River Wye (SK 161729), formerly a cotton spinning mill and now used for the processing of nylon yarns, see p 110. Cressbrook Mill also on the Wye (SK 173726), established for cotton manufacturing by Arkwright probably in 1783, is described on p 109 (plate, p 90).

Water. The partial remains of a water-powered system for pumping spring water from the Wye Valley to Cressbrook village above can be seen at SK 166729 (see p 124).

LONGNOR

Quarrying. There is a small disused parish quarry, formerly worked for millstone grit for local use, behind Daisy Knoll Farm (SK 083651). Men from Longnor for many years travelled daily to work at the large Hindlow Quarry south of Buxton.

Mill. A corn mill on the River Dove at Glutton Bridge (SK 084665) was demolished in the 1940s.

Leather. Saddlery and shoemaking were apparently of importance in Longnor (see p 120).

Agriculture. Walled narrow strips of land on the hillside above the River Manifold, south-east of the village, are believed to be remains of a former area of open field cultivation.

There was a square pinfold on the south-east side of the village; two walls only now remain, the other boundaries are marked by trees, and the former entrance place, now blocked up but still visible (SK 090649).

LYME HANDLEY   (All of the parish except the north-west)

This is mainly an agricultural parish although in bygone days many people worked in the Lumb Cotton Mill, just over the boundary in Kettleshulme.

MACCLESFIELD FOREST

Quarrying. There are various minor quarry workings for millstone grit.

Water. The parish contains most of the Trentabank Reservoir (SJ 963713) and part of the Lamaload (SJ 973747), see p 134.

MELTHAM   (South-west)

Mining. Two very thin seams of coal called the Upper Meltham Coal and the Lower Meltham Coal respectively—the lower of them the lowest seam ever mined in Yorkshire—were mined at Brow Grains in the first half of the nineteenth century. The coming of the railway bringing cheap coal from Huddersfield ended the industry here.

Quarrying. Besides various small millstone grit quarries used formerly for building stone and road metal there are the gannister workings on Royd Edge, described on p 93.

Mill. New Bridge Mill, known also as 'The Panner' (SE 088107) was in use for the manufacture of woollen cloth until the late 1960s.

Water. One of the catchwater conduits which Huddersfield Waterworks Commissioners obtained permission to dig for supplementing Blackmoorfoot Reservoir in 1869 is crossed by the road at SE 092100. Known locally as the 'catch' the conduit was designed to pick up the water from streams at about the 850ft level. In fact, the 'catch' has never caught any water for the first few hundred yards of its length due to a lack of available springs, hence its dry state. Water catchment begins, however, shortly after the road crossing, and where it crosses Brow Grains Dyke a dam and series of sluices allow it to take part of the water but not all from the dyke; at this point it is also periodically supplemented by water pumped from a number of boreholes running along the line of a fault (SE 082105).

MIDDLETON & SMERRILL

Mining. Remains of lead mining include workings on Long Rake in the north and others scattered throughout the parish. There is a disused umber mine at SK 190613.

Quarrying. In addition to small disused limestone quarries on Middleton Common there are the signs of past and present workings for silica, and the route of the former tramway system from the Friden works can be faintly traced (see p 80).

Mills, etc. There was formerly a corn mill at SK 199636 on the River Bradford, where its site is marked by some slight ruins. At SK 199633 there is the shell of a building which formerly contained a waterwheel used for pumping spring water up to Middleton village. Between these two sites there was a bobbin mill and a cotton tape mill but no signs of these remain.

Lace making was formerly a cottage industry of Middleton (see p 116).

Agriculture. Sheep were washed in the River Bradford at SK 199633 where there are still remains of the collecting pens. Sheep were brought here from some distance around until the practice ceased in the inter-war years. Land nearby, called Gooseholme, is said to have been used for grazing geese.

Communications. The route of the Derby–Buxton Roman road forms the parish boundary on the west.

MILLERS DALE—see WORMHILL; TADDINGTON; TIDESWELL

MONYASH

Mining. There are considerable lead-mining remains throughout the parish including Knotlow and Hillocks Mines (SK 144674 and 145672). Ore was reputedly washed in a pool marked now by a boggy depression at SK 143673 (see p 44). Monyash was the centre for the High Peak Barmote Court. A building at SK 150667, opposite the chapel, was where miners were paid.

Quarrying. There are many small limestone quarries in the parish and formerly numerous 'pudding-pie' limekilns. One kiln in a field at SK 155675, still in recognisable condition, was used as a model for an exhibit in Derby Museum.

Crinoidal limestone or 'marble' was formerly obtained in the Ricklow Quarry in Lathkill Dale (SK 165661) until workings collapsed around 1900, and also at Brecks Quarry (SK 148677) which supplied stone for public buildings in various parts of the country.

Ropewalk. The site of a ropewalk is marked by a raised grass verge beneath trees on the west side of the lane leading north from Cross Lanes (SK 146667). Ropemaking ended here in the nineteenth century.

Candle factory. For the former candle factory at SK 149664 see p 122.

Agriculture. There is a good example of an ancient parish mere in the village (SK 150664).

Sheep were formerly washed in the River Lathkill at SK 174655 near the footbridge below One Ash Grange.

The remaining walls of a pinfold can be seen beside the road north of the village (SK 149669).

Communications. The route of the Derby–Buxton Roman road forms part of the parish boundary on the west.

A stone building at SK 147665 was formerly a toll bar house.

NETHER HADDON

Mining. There are remains of past lead mining, particularly in the south of the parish. A northward extension of Wheel's Rake at the back of Shining Bank Quarry was worked until the 1880s.

Quarrying. Nutseats Quarry (SK 237658) beside the A6 south-west of Haddon Hall is now a repository for vehicles, etc. Shining Bank Quarry (SK 228649) is currently worked.

Communications. The disused Midland Railway line runs through the parish and includes the 1,058yd long Haddon Tunnel.

NETHER PADLEY

Quarrying. There are remains of workings for millstone grit along the edge in the east of the parish.

Communications. A well-preserved example of a toll house with projecting windows can be seen at Grindleford Bridge (SK 245778).

NEW MILLS   (Thornsett and Rowarth Wards)

Mining. Coal was formerly mined on the hillsides, usually by tunnels; these had ventilation shafts which are now filled in.

Quarrying. There are various old quarry workings.

Mills. There were five cotton mills in the valley at Rowarth in the early nineteenth century; in 1857 there were two cotton mills and one paper mill but by the end of the century there were none. Some ruins still remain close by the stream. By the Little Mill Inn (SK 011889) is the site of a waterwheel and of other mill structures now demolished. At SK 015900 is a former mill dam; ruins below it are of Rowarth Grove Mill, said to have been a calico printing works.

At SK 009893 is the site of the Alma Mount Bleachworks and the remains of the dam.

Agriculture. Rowarth was one of the areas said to have been land-drained by unemployed labour during the 'cotton panic', as was other land near Glossop (see under Charlesworth parish, p 198).

NEWTON GRANGE

Communications. The disused track of the former L & NW railway from Ashbourne to Buxton runs through the parish with the demolished Alsop-en-le-Dale station at SK 156548. Closed to passengers on 1 November 1954 and for goods on 7 October 1963 the station is now a car park for the 'Tissington Trail' (see p 176).

ONECOTE   (Excluding a small portion of the parish in the south-west)

Mining. There are remains of copper mining at Mixon (SK 046574), see p 59.

Quarrying. A quarry west of Mixon and various small pits on the hillside of the Hamps Valley were worked for local use and limestone from these sources was burnt in numerous small kilns in the fields (see p 64).

Mill. A building near the village, at SK 047554, was formerly a corn mill; the mill house is still inhabited.

Agriculture. Onecote is one of the last parishes in the national park where sheep were washed. This was done in the River Hamps, between the village and Mixon, and also, in the latter days, at Ford. The site at Ford (SK 063539), close to Banktop, was a natural one and ideal for the job; the sheep entered the river beneath a bridge over a tributary stream at a point where the river's depth made damming unnecessary, and left the water on the opposite bank.

OUTSEATS

Smelting. The name Bole Hill, on the western side of the parish, suggests a former smelting site.

Quarrying. There are a few small disused gritstone quarries including one at Callow Bank (SK 252823).

Millstones were cut on Stanage Edge and there are a number of good abandoned examples to be seen above Overstones Farm (SK 249830), see p 82 and plate, p 54.

Mill. The Green's House Paper Mill (SK 233837) is described on p 97.

Agriculture. Sheep were washed near Sheepwash Bank at a point where a stream coming down from Stanage Edge joins the main brook (SK 233843).

OVER HADDON

Mining. There are extensive remains of lead mining, particularly of the Mandale Mine, including various features in Lathkill Dale. At SK 205661 is the collapsed tail of the Lathkill Dale Sough, marked by undulating ground; the sough discharged here after passing under the river from the south side a short distance upstream. Farther up the dale, at SK 197661, are the Mandale Sough tail (plate, p17) and engine house shell; and at SK 195660 stone pillars of the launder which brought water across the river for powering a waterwheel (see p 45). All were connected with mines on Mandale Rake, undulations of which can be seen on the hillside above, south-east from Haddon Grove Farm. Still farther up the dale there are on the north bank remains of old shafts, the ruins of a powder house (SK 194658) and at SK 191657 the site of a 52ft waterwheel used for unwatering the Lathkill Dale Mine, marked now only by some of the wheelpit walling and remains of stone pillars which supported the launder.

Quarrying. There are various small quarries including 'marble' workings in Lathkill Dale (SK 188658).

Mills. Carter's Mill (SK 184657), now demolished, was a corn mill dating from the early nineteenth century. Although long in disuse the building still stood up to World War II when the waterwheel was removed for scrap. Subsequently the walls disintegrated and most of the stones were removed. Two millstones remain on the site, close to the weir.

Sough Mill, close to Lathkill Lodge (SK 203662) dates at least from 1529 and was worked until the early nineteenth century. The weir is still prominent and wooden workings still exist within the building which is used as a gamekeeper's store.

There was a further mill at Conksbury, upstream from Coalpit Bridge, but only the weir remains.

Agriculture. Sheep were washed in the Lathkill at various points: at SK 174654 where Cales Dale joins the Lathkill, above the waterfall by Carter's Mill, by Lathkill Lodge, and above Conksbury Bridge (SK 212655). Sheep washing was done at the first and last of these places at least until after World War II. Stone holding pens can still be seen at the Conksbury Bridge site, on the west bank of the river.

There was a pinfold (always known as 'the pound') at the west end of the village, by the green and tea shop; it is now partly built over, though portions of wall remain (SK 203664).

PARWICH

Mining. There are old lead-mining shafts amongst trees on Parwich Hill (SK 188550) and also slight remains in the area of Lombard's Green and Roystone Rocks, north of the village.

Quarrying. There are numerous small disused limestone quarries which were worked in the past for building stone. Many Parwich men also formerly worked in the quarries which existed at Alsop-en-le-Dale.

Sandpits at Lowmoor (SK 190565 and 186571) were worked until recent years.

Agriculture. Sheep were formerly washed close to the village where a small stream was dammed. The site, still locally called 'the Dam', is now mainly dry and weed grown, the area surrounding is still walled although sheep pens which existed in the past have been removed.

Communications. A section of the disused Cromford & High Peak Railway including the Gotham curve (see p 170) is in the north of the parish.

PEAK FOREST   (All of the parish except the extreme south-west)

Mining. There are considerable remains of lead mining, comprising hillocks and old shafts, including those of Oxlow (SK 129808, etc) around Eldon Hill.

Quarrying. There are various small quarry workings, and more extensive ones in the south-west of the parish verging on Dove Holes Dale. (Eldon Hill Quarry is modern.)

Mills. Although the corn mill itself is gone the modernised mill cottage remains as a dwelling (SK 115787) and water still flows from the dam.

Agriculture. Sheep are said to have been washed in the stream immediately above the mill where remains of stone-walled enclosures can be seen. There was another sheep washing place north of the

B6061 at Perryfoot (SK 100813) where a south-flowing stream on the west side was diverted to water it when required.

POTT SHRIGLEY   (The south-eastern two-thirds of the parish)

Mining. Remains of coal-mining shafts exist on the moorland north of Bakestonedale (see p 92). Also to be seen on the Bakestonedale hillside are disused fireclay excavations; the works where the clay was made into tiles, firebricks and furnace linings border the road through the dale (SJ 952796), see p 94.

Quarrying. Amongst quarries, mostly disused, is the Klondyke Quarry (SJ 961790), opened around 1900. Its roughish stone was worked particularly for kerb and paving stones. Small quantities are still extracted, for ornamental and other purposes.

Mill. There is believed to have been a corn mill long ago at Overhayes (formerly Pott Mill) Farm (SJ 947797).

QUARNFORD

Mining. Considerable signs of ground disturbance, particularly on Goldsitch Moss, are the remains of past coal mining.

Mill. For Gradbach Mill, on the River Dane (SK 994661), formerly a silk mill, see p 118.

The covering of buttons with fine silk braid was a one-time cottage industry (see p 116).

Pinfold. The old pinfold, now containing rubbish, is by the old road west of Flash.

RAINOW   (All of the parish except the extreme west)

Mining. There were coal pits in the vicinity of Harrop (see p 92).

Quarrying. A number of small millstone grit quarries were worked in the past for local building stone.

Deposits of a white substance similar to china clay were worked on land owned by a Peter Orme in the north of the parish, near Harrop, from about 1779. Near the site, Orme established the Whiteland Tileries where the material was used for making sinks, tiles and ornamentation until the middle of the nineteenth century.

Mills. Swift flowing water from the hills formerly powered many mills in Rainow, though most of them were situated in the part of the parish outside today's national park. Silk throwing, cotton spinning, weaving and dyeing were important.

At Brookhouse Clough (SJ 947751) there were two mills. One was used by Joseph Broster as a dye works, the other, larger mill, was bought in the nineteenth century by a Mr Neave and fitted up for making hats (see p 123). After the business moved to Bollington in about 1873 most of the mill was demolished, a mainly new house built and gardens laid out. Part of the mill's second storey was retained to form a terrace walk overlooking the garden and the old ivy-clad mill chimney and the site of the waterfall into the wheelpit still exists practically untouched. Also in these private grounds, in the clough above the house, is the site of the small mill dam (now silted) and remains of the sluices, and, close by, the small building where dyeing was done.

At Mill Brook (SJ 949757) there was a cotton mill, said to have been three times burnt down, the last time in about 1868. The proprietor was a Stephen Sheldon whose son brought the raw cotton from Manchester by waggons and teams of horses. After the last fire a portion of the buildings was rebuilt and used by another firm as a fustian-cutting room. There was formerly a very high chimney. There are no remains of the mill. A water pumping station now occupies the site; when foundations for this were being dug a pipe, believed to have been for gas, was discovered from which it is conjectured that the mill had gas lighting.

For Gin Clough Mill (SJ 958764), formerly worked for silk, see p 117.

Water. Part of the modern Lamaload Reservoir lies within the parish (see p 134).

Agriculture. The rapid growth of Macclesfield during the Industrial Revolution caused a great increase in the sale of butter and cheese from Rainow farms. The area around Saltersford was particularly noted for its cheese production.

Communications. The parish saw much and varied packhorse traffic in bygone days. For Saltersford see p 162.

ROWLAND

Mining. There are some remains of lead mining including those of Oxpasture Mine, west of the village (SK 212722).

Communications. The disused Midland Railway line passes through the south of the parish.

ROWSLEY

Mill. The Rowsley Corn Mill (SK 255657) is owned by the Haddon Estate and has been run by Messrs Caudwell Ltd as a flour mill since the present building was constructed in 1870 or 1871. It is believed there was previously a sawmill on the site, but many records were unfortunately burnt in the inter-war years. Buildings on the south side are apparently older than the main one. There is no memory of the waterwheel but its position and marks left by its use are still visible; evidently undershot, it must have been of 12–14ft diameter and of about the same width. The waterwheel has long been replaced by turbines, the present two, of 80 and 50hp respectively, both about 50 years old, are still powered by the River Wye. Milling is now performed by rollers in place of the original stones; flour is milled and maize and barley are ground, and animal feeding stuffs are made up to supply various products for which the firm is agent.

Dairy. The milk factory of Express Dairies Ltd (SK 259658) has been disused since 1968.

Communications. The disused Midland Railway line passes through the parish. The passenger section of Rowsley station (just outside the parish and area boundary on the east) was closed on 6 March 1967 and the goods depot on 1 July 1968.

SADDLEWORTH   (Eastern section)

Quarrying. There are a number of disused millstone grit quarries. Runninghill Pits (SE 016074), also known as Denman Quarries and Fairy Holes (due to a fable about moor sprites), were worked for roadstone in the nineteenth century. They were opened for supplying material for a road planned to run across the moors to Meltham, construction on which provided relief work for the unemployed in the 1860s. But, after starting, the project was considered impracticable due to the depth of peat on the moor, and the scheme was abandoned.

Mill. Diggle Mill (SE 017080) was formerly a woollen mill with a very large waterwheel demolished in about 1920. The water reserve or lodge and the wheelpit still remain, as well as part of the original building which now houses a plastics factory.

Water. In the area are the Yeoman Hay (SE 022050), Greenfield (SE 029053), Chew (SE 038020) and Dove Stone (SE 016037) Reservoirs (see p 133).

The Diggle Reservoir (SE 021081) and the Little Black Moss (SE 031086) were constructed as feeders for the Huddersfield Canal and the Brun Clough (SE 018093) as a compensation reservoir.

SHATTON—see BROUGH & SHATTON

SHEEN

Quarrying. Millstone grit quarries at SK 109606 were abandoned earlier this century. Besides having a considerable local use the stone was carted away for building purposes to places far afield, including Leek. It was also used for making stone launders for Ecton Mine (see p 58).

Mill. Brund Mill (SK 099613) on the River Manifold, bears the date 1762. There was formerly a corn mill on the site but from the end of the eighteenth century the premises comprised a cotton factory, believed to have been leased by a Thomas Cantrell and used by him and his three sons for cotton spinning and calico making. Since that time the building has reputedly been used as a sawmill, and during wartime for grinding corn. The large derelict building now remains in a semi-ruinous state; the site of the wheelpit is apparent but the mill dam is overgrown (plate, p 89).

Agriculture. Sheep were formerly washed in the River Manifold.

SHEFFIELD (Extreme west)

Quarrying. Various disused gritstone quarries include the Brown Edge Quarries (SK 276839) and the Millstone Quarries near Hathersage (SK 248800–248808). The latter are described on pp 84, 88.

Water. For the Redmires Reservoirs (SK 258855, 262855 and 268853) and the Rivelin Dams (SK 270868 and 274867) see p 127.

SHELDON

Mining. There are considerable remains of lead mining including those verging on the Magpie Mine to the south (see Ashford-in-the-Water), also Kirk Dale Mine (SK 182688) and Fieldgrove Mine (SK 173693). The Magpie Sough tail is seen at SK 179696 (see p 45).

Quarrying. Rosewood 'marble' was formerly extracted in Nettler Dale, not far from the Magpie Sough tail, but the workings are very overgrown.

Mills. Two buildings on the south bank of the River Wye (SK 182696), the more westerly of them still retaining two external iron waterwheels, formerly comprised a bone mill (see p 99) and were latterly used for timber. The leat is still traceable coming from the weir across the river a short distance upstream.

Water. Close to the river, beside the mill buildings just described, is a pumping house and small waterwheel used in the past for raising spring water to Sheldon village (see pp 124, 127).

Pinfold. A pinfold is said to have existed at the top end of the village, but no signs of it remain.

SMERRILL—see MIDDLETON & SMERRILL

SNITTERTON—see WENSLEY & SNITTERTON

SPARROWPIT—see CHAPEL-EN-LE-FRITH

STANTON   (All of the parish except the extreme south-east)

Mining. There are a number of old lead-mining shafts along the parish's western boundary. On the east, in Hillcarr Wood (SK 258637) is the tail of the Hillcarr Sough (see p 45).

Quarrying. There is a large limekiln with trees growing out of its stonework on the east side of the A524 road (SK 231639) and another beside the same road, $\frac{1}{2}$ mile farther north (SK 231646). In the east of the parish there are extensive millstone grit quarries (see p 85) and a number of discarded grindstones can be found.

Mill. The shell of an ancient and long-disused limestone-built corn mill stands a short distance to the east of the A524 (SK 233639).

Leather. Ornamental leather work in the form of flowers and fruit was at one time a cottage industry of Stanton. Examples of such work can be seen in the Bakewell Old House Museum.

STOKE

Quarrying. For the millstone grit Stoke Quarry (SK 236769) see p 85.

STONEY MIDDLETON

Mining and Smelting. There are considerable remains of lead mining. At Sallet Hole Mine in Coombs Dale (SK 219741) an eighteenth-century level penetrating Deep Rake has been enlarged and is currently worked for fluorspar by Laporte Industries Ltd, whose large Cavendish Mill processing plant is situated a short distance away on Middleton Moor (SK 206752), see p 56.

Some remains still exist in Middleton Dale of the former cupola and Lords' smelt mill (SK 224756) and of another cupola and slag mill on a site owned by Eyam Quarries Ltd (SK 212758), see p 49.

Quarrying. Modern limestone quarrying which has swept away a number of earlier limekilns continues as an important industry in Middleton Dale.

Mill, etc. The former Carters Corn Mill (SK 230755), with water still rushing down at its side although the waterwheel was removed by early this century, has, for many years, been a footwear factory (see p 121). An empty building on the south side of the main road through the village (SK 229755) was one of about four other such factories which in the past existed at Stoney Middleton.

SWINSCOE—see BLORE WITH SWINSCOE

TADDINGTON

Mining. Remains of lead mining in the form of old shafts and hillocks are numerous throughout the parish. Occurrence of the word 'Wheal' in the south (Nether Wheal and Over Wheal) is of interest; an old Cornish word for mine, it is very commonly found in the names of mines in Cornwall and Devon.

Quarrying. There are a number of small workings for limestone and there were limekilns in many of the fields in days gone by.

For the Millers Dale Limeworks (SK 143732) see pp 73–4 and plate, p 53.

Rope or Hessian works. At Taddington Hall, in the village (SK 146711), there is believed formerly to have been a hessian or rope works contained in the present saddle room and in extensive cellars beneath the house. Two brothers reputedly ran the business, one was responsible for the manufacturing while the other travelled with the goods. It is said that the one who travelled arrived home one night intoxicated, having presumably spent the proceeds on drinking, and that during an ensuing argument he murdered his brother whose ghost is reported still to roam.

Agriculture. A fine example of early terraced cultivation, described on p 138, can be seen north of the A6 at Priestcliffe (SK 142717).

There was formerly a pinfold in the village but its identity has become lost since being sold by the parish council some years ago.

Communications. The disused Midland Railway line, with the double viaduct at Millers Dale, passes through the north of the parish (plate, p 144).

THORNHILL

Besom making. Part of an old building called 'The Moot' (SK 198835) was formerly used as a workshop for the making of besoms.

Agriculture. In the past there was a sheep washing place in the River Derwent downstream from Yorkshire Bridge.

Water/Communications. The route of the railway used during construction of the Howden and Derwent dams, early this century, can be traced. A bridge which carried the line across the road at SK 197840 was removed in about 1950; part of the brick supports can still be seen.

THORPE

Quarrying. Weary Grebes Quarry (SK 162513), formerly worked for building stone, has been disused since about 1900; lime-burning was formerly done in the vicinity. The small quarry at SK 156507 was last worked during World War II.

Mill. Thorpe Corn Mill on the River Dove (SK 146505) has been completely demolished except for a portion of walling to which has been added an agricultural shed; the millstream can still be seen. The mill was last worked in about 1893.

Agriculture. Sheep were formerly washed in the Dove at the Stepping Stones (SK 151514) and below Coldwall Bridge (SK 150498) where signs of stone walling by the bank, and of pens, can still be discerned. Washing was last done here in the 1950s.

'Ridge and furrow' undulations in a number of grass fields, particularly in the east of the parish, are evidence of past ploughing.

The former pinfold, somewhat altered, adjoins a house at the south end of the village (SK 155500).

Communications. An old coach road formerly passed through the village, entering via Church Lane, crossing the present road near the church and continuing south-westwards down the hillside through a field, where its route in the form of a depression can be seen. The road crossed the Dove by Coldwall Bridge (see p 165 and plate, p 143).

The disused track of the former L & NW railway from Ashbourne to Buxton runs through the east of the parish, now the 'Tissington Trail' (see p 176). Thorpe Cloud station (SK 165503), now demolished, was closed to passengers on 1 November 1954 and for goods on 7 October 1963.

TIDESWELL

Mining. There are remains of lead mining throughout the parish, but more concentrated in the north on Tideswell Moor, on the Peak Forest boundary and along Tideslow Rake.

Quarrying. In addition to smaller workings for limestone, the quarry in Tideswell Dale was worked in the past for basalt (see under Litton, and p 77).

Mills, etc. Tideswell Corn Mill beside the River Wye (SK 142733), built of limestone, is in an advanced state of disrepair. The dilapidated waterwheel, iron framed with wood paddles, of approximately 11ft diameter and 6ft width, is still in situ; the mill race is dry, although a little water appears in the tail race. Owned by Dakins, the mill probably ceased working at about the time of World War I.

The factory at Summer Cross (SK 149756), said to have been originally called Rising Sun, was formerly a cotton, velvet or fustian-cutting factory. The long sɯooɹ contained tables about 30ft in length on which the uncut material was spread, and the workers walked up and down cutting the tiny loops in the fabric with a special type of knife made from a clock spring. The work ceased in the 1930s. During World War II the building housed poultry and then became a plastics factory specialising in injection moulding and making knife handles, etc, and later perspex brush packs and industrial gloves. Now, much altered internally, it is used by the Buisman Coffee Company.

A small factory on the Manchester road (SK 147763) was formerly a calico weaving factory. It is now used for the making of steel magnets by Swift Levick & Company. (The curious conical object nearby surrounds the intake of the village's former water supply.)

Silk weaving was important in the past (see p 115); a private workshop in the village was at one time a small silk factory.

The woodcarving business of Messrs Hunstone has been a family concern for some generations, specialising mainly in work for churches over a wide area including a memorial to George Stephenson in Holy Trinity Church, Chesterfield. The present premises in Tideswell's Market Square were formerly the Marquess of Granby Inn; the older part of the building has mullion windows and probably dates from 1600, the later part is believed to be eighteenth century.

Agriculture. The remains of a specially constructed sheepwash can be seen beside the Manchester road (SK 145768).

The remains of a roughly rectangular pinfold adjoins the Pinfold housing estate (SK 152751).

Communications. The route of the Batham Gate Roman road passes across the north of the parish.

P

TINTWISTLE   (All of the parish except the extreme south-west)

Quarrying. Several disused millstone grit quarries include the Tintwistle Knarr Quarry (SK 044993) used for much building, including Mottram Church. Many formerly private quarries were taken over by Manchester Corporation when the reservoirs were being constructed and the stone used in the building of walls, bridges and watercourses.

Mills/Water. A number of mills in the Longdendale Valley were dismantled and submerged by construction of the reservoirs (see p 129). The northern sections of the Woodhead (SK 090995), Torside (SK 070988), Rhodeswood (SK 050982), Vale House (SK 037978) and Bottoms (SK 025970) Reservoirs lie within the parish.

Agriculture. The use of sheep washing places in the Longdendale Valley was prohibited by the reservoirs' construction. There are faint traces of former sheepwashes in some of the feeder streams.

Communications. Part of the Woodhead Tunnel and its western portals are in the parish (see pp 171–4 and plate, p 144).

TISSINGTON

Quarrying. The limestone quarry at Rushy Cliff (SK 176533) supplied stone for local building requirements.

Beside a small quarry in a field in the west of the parish (SK 156525) is a substantial limekiln.

Mill. For Woodeaves Mill (SK 184504) see p 113.

Agriculture. Pronounced 'ridge and furrow' undulations in many of the grass fields are evidence of past ploughing. These are particularly noticeable west of the A515 road opposite the turnings to Tissington village.

Communications. The disused track of the former L & NW railway from Ashbourne to Buxton runs through the east of the parish, now the 'Tissington Trail' (see p 176). Tissington station (SK 177520),

now demolished, was closed for both passengers and goods on
1 November 1954.

UPPER HULME—see LEEKFRITH; HEATHYLEE

WARDLOW

Mining. There are considerable remains of lead mining in the form
of shafts and hillocks.

Pinfold. The former small pinfold now forms part of a private
garden (SK 182746).

WARSLOW & ELKSTONES

Mining. Dale Lead Mine (SK 093587) to the west of the River
Manifold was last worked, it is believed, in the 1880s. Shafts and
mounds remain on the hillside.

There were also lead mines on the hills above Upper Elkstone in
the vicinity of New York (SK 048591). The old count house here
remains, in a ruinous state.

Quarrying. Local stone was quarried and broken by hand for roadmaking until the 1930s. Previously the limestone was used considerably in kilns of which there were several on the hillsides above the
River Hamps, mostly now disappeared.

Mill. Four millstones and some fragments of foundation walls by
some hawthorn trees beside the Warslow Brook mark the site of
Warslow or Brownlow Corn Mill (SK 075576). The position of the
leat and mill pond can be determined.

Agriculture. Sheep were formerly washed close to the mill.

WATERHOUSES (North-east)

Mining. There are a few shaft remains of copper and lead mining
on the hills north of Back-of-the-Brook; a level formerly opened in
the valley.

Some undulations at Ironpits (SK 067520) mark the site of former workings for iron. It is believed that iron from here was smelted at the former foundry at Winkhill.

Quarrying. The limestone quarry near Greensides (SK 090503) has long since ceased production. Another quarry nearer the village (SK 086503), where two kilns survive, was used more recently.

Pinfold. The pinfold near Waterfall (SK 082513) is recognisable, but filled with ashes.

Communications. Waterhouses was the starting point of the Leek & Manifold Valley Light Railway, the route of which is followed by the footpath up the Hamps Valley (see pp 176–9).

WENSLEY & SNITTERTON

Mining. There are considerable remains of lead mining, including the Old Mill Close Mine, with the ruins of its engine house (SK 258618).

WETTON

Mining. The site of the important Ecton Copper Mine (centred on SK 100580, see pp 57–9) is the hill bordered on the west by the road down the Manifold Valley to Wetton Mill, from which various features are visible. Beside the Back of Ecton road, on the east side of Ecton Hill, can be seen the 'fish pond' which was a reservoir for ore-washing water (SK 104581), the remains of East Ecton Mine (SK 103584) and former miners' cottages. Besides working in the mines these cottagers each farmed 7–8 acres of land, keeping a cow or two and fattening a pig, and also at times independently surface-worked for lead.

Quarrying. There are various disused limestone workings including quarries at Ecton. A quarry north-west of Wetton village (SK 107557), which closed in the 1940s, was in earlier days used for making stone paving setts (see p 60); limeburning was also done and there are the remains of a kiln.

Mills, etc. Wetton Mill, formerly also called Ecton Mill (SK 096561), ceased as a corn mill by the end of the nineteenth century. Much rebuilt, it is now a farm.

Some of the old buildings in the village were reputedly used in the past for linen and cotton manufacture, and there is said to have been a button factory in the top floor of the Manor House.

Cheese factory. At Ecton is the site of a former cheese factory (SK 096583), see p 155.

Communications. Short lengths of the footpath on the route of the former Leek and Manifold Valley Light Railway pass within the parish, at Ecton and south of Wetton Mill.

WHESTON

Mining. Remains of lead mining occur throughout the parish.

Communications. The minor road across the south of the parish is an old coach road; in 1790 a stage coach travelled along it on alternate days from Buxton to Sheffield, via Hargatewall, Tideswell and Eyam. Horses were changed near Monksdale House.

WILDBOARCLOUGH

Mining. Coal has been mined at various places in the parish, including Holt (where there remains an old square chimney, south-east of the A54 road, SK 009699), Knar and Cumberland.

Quarrying. There are a number of workings for millstone grit including the Danebower Quarries (SK 013700).

Mills. Both the Lower Crag Mill (SJ 983686) for which James Brindley installed the engineering system, and the upper mill buildings (SJ 983687) used formerly for silk and latterly for carpet manufacture, are now demolished. Administrative buildings survive as the Wildboarclough Post Office (see pp 116–17).

Agriculture. Sheep are said to have been washed in the Clough Brook in former times.

WINCLE

Mill. Folly Mill (SJ 971664), a former paper mill, is in ruins (see pp 97–8).

Pinfold. There are the remains of a small rectangular pinfold east of the road at SJ 957663.

WINSTER

Mining. There are considerable remains of lead mining, with numerous old shafts throughout the parish.

Cotton. A building which is believed formerly to have been a cotton mill stands at the top of Woolley's Yard (SK 241605).

Candle factory. A candle factory, little of which remains, is said to have been sited adjacent to the cotton mill (SK 241605).

WORMHILL   (Excluding the west of the parish)

Smelting. Bole Hill was probably a smelting place.

Quarrying. Most of the parish's limestone quarrying area lies outside the national park. An exception is the former East Buxton Limeworks (see p 73), where two large kilns remain, adjacent to the railway (SK 133732).

Mill. Wormhill Corn Mill on the River Wye in Millers Dale (SK 137732) originated at least five centuries ago, King John having given a mill at Wormhill to Daniel Pincerna. The present mill building dates from 1860; it was owned by Ben and William Dakin and is now used by Staffordshire Farmers. The waterwheel was removed some years ago.

James Brindley, the canal pioneer, is reputed to have been born and to have lived as a child in a cottage, now demolished, near Tunstead. The site is marked by a plaque erected by the Derbyshire Archaeological Society (SK 109749).

YOULGREAVE

Mining. There are considerable remains of lead mining throughout the parish.

Paper mill, etc. There was formerly a paper mill at Alport, just above the bridge on the north bank of the River Lathkill, but no sign remains. Weaving sheds were nearby and also a dye house.

Agriculture. Sheep were washed in the River Bradford above Rheinstor Rock (SK 218643).

The former village pinfold still exists immediately west of the Methodist Church (SK 206641).

Communications. The Coalpit packhorse bridge (SK 215652), and others at Bradford (SK 215641) and at Alport (SK 222645) still remain.

References and Bibliography

Abbreviations

Bull PDMHS	*Bulletin* of the Peak District Mines Historical Society
DAJ	*Journal* of the Derbyshire Archaeological Society
DM	*Derbyshire Miscellany* The Bulletin of the Local History Section of the Derbyshire Archaeological Society
Trans NS	*Transactions* of the Newcomen Society for the History of Technology
DC	*Derbyshire Countryside*

GENERAL

Farey, John. *General View of the Agriculture and Minerals of Derbyshire*, vols 1, 2 and 3 (1815)
Victoria History of Derbyshire, vol 1 (1905), vol 2 (1907)
Victoria History of Staffordshire
White's Directories

CHAPTER ONE (*A Sublime Source*. Page 13)

Peak District National Park Development Plan (1955)
Peak District National Park Guide (1960)
Edwards, K. C. *The Peak District* (1962)

CHAPTER TWO (*Metalliferous Mining*. Page 27)

Daniel, Clarence. 'Epics of the Edgeside Vein', *DC* (June–July 1958)
Ford, Trevor D. 'Blue John Fluorspar', Yorkshire Geological Society, vol 30, pt 1, no 4 (15 Sept 1955)
Kirkham, Nellie. *Derbyshire Lead Mining through the Centuries* (Truro, 1968)
Kirkham, Nellie. 'Great Hucklow Mines', *Bull PDMHS*, 2 no 1 (1963–5)
Kirkham, Nellie. 'Eyam Edge Mines and Soughs Part I', *Bull PDMHS*, 2 pt 5 (May 1965)
Kirkham, Nellie. 'Eyam Edge Mines and Soughs Part II', *Bull PDMHS*, 2 pt 6 (Dec 1965)
Kirkham, Nellie. 'Eyam Edge Mines and Soughs Part III', *Bull PDMHS*, 3 pt 1 (July 1966)
Kirkham, Nellie. 'Eyam Edge Mines and Soughs Part IV', *Bull PDMHS*, 3 pt 2 (Dec 1966)
Kirkham, Nellie. 'Soughs in Middleton Dale Part I', *Bull PDMHS*, 3 pt 6 (1968)
Kirkham, Nellie. 'Longstone Edge Area Mines and Soughs Part I', British Speleo-

logical Association Journal *Cave Science*, 5 no 39 (1966), 354–68 and 'Part II', 5 no 40, 440–69

Kirkham, Nellie. 'The Ventilation of Hillcarr Sough', *Trans NS*, 37 (1964–5)

Kirkham, Nellie. 'Steam Engines in Derbyshire Lead Mines', *Trans NS*, 38 (1965–6)

Kirkham, Nellie and Ford, Trevor D. 'The Ecton Copper Mines', *PDMHS Special Publication No 1* (2nd ed, 1967)

Peak District Mines Historical Society. *Lead Mining in the Peak District* (1968)

Porter, Lindsey. 'Ecton Hill—A Study of the Surface Features', *Bull PDMHS*, 4 pt 2 (Nov 1969)

Radley, Jeffrey. 'The Transport of Lead: A Contribution to the Geography of Lead Mining', *Bull PDMHS*, 2 no 1 (1963–5)

Rieuwerts, James H. 'Lathkill Dale: Its Mines and Mining', *Bull PDMHS*, 2 no 1 (1963–5) and Supplementary Notes, 3 pt 1 (July 1966)

Rieuwerts, James H. 'A List of the Soughs of Derbyshire Lead Mines', *Bull PDMHS*, 3 pt 1 (July 1966)

Rieuwerts, James H. 'The Soughs of Derbyshire Lead Mines. A Supplementary List', *Bull PDMHS*, 4 pt 2 (Nov 1969)

Robey, J. A. 'The Ecton Copper Mines in the Seventeenth Century', *Bull PDMHS*, 4 pt 2 (Nov 1969)

Willies, L. 'Winster and 18th Century Lead Mines', *Bull PDMHS*, 3 pt 5 (May 1968)

Willies, L. 'Cupola Lead Smelting Sites in Derbyshire 1737–1900', *Bull PDMHS*, 4 pt 1 (March 1969)

Leek Local History Library. *Ecton Hill Copper Mine*, William Efford, 1769. Transscribed by B. Bentley (*The Staffordshire Teacher*, Dec 1955)

CHAPTER THREE (*Exploitation of the Rock Formations*. Page 60)

Ford, Trevor D. 'The Black Marble of Ashford-in-the-Water, Derbyshire', Liverpool & Manchester Geological *Journal*, 2 pt 1 (30 Jan 1958)

Ford, Trevor D. 'The Black Marble of Ashford-in-the-Water', *Bull PDMHS*, 2 no 4 (Oct 1964)

Jackson, Leslie. 'The Buxton Lime Trade', *Cement, Lime and Gravel* (Oct and Nov 1950)

Radley, Jeffery. 'Peak Millstones and Hallamshire Grindstones', *Trans NS*, 36 (1963–4)

Radley, Jeffery. 'A Millstone Maker's Smithy on Gardom's Edge, Baslow', *DAJ*, 84 (1964)

Ripley, D. *The Peak Forest Tramway* (Lingfield)

1 Information kindly supplied by Mr W. A. Billington, Museum Curator, Messrs Josiah Wedgwood & Sons Ltd.

2 From the Notebook of William Boulsover, Secretary to the Bakewell Field Club, late nineteenth and early twentieth centuries.

CHAPTER FOUR (*Mills and Manufacturing*. Page 95)

Ashmore, Owen. 'The Early Textile Industry in the Derwent Valley', *DM*, 1 no 5 (March 1957)

Ashmore, Owen. 'The Early Textile Industry in North-west Derbyshire', *DM*, 1 no 9 (June 1958)
Bellhouse, Marguerite A. Life. *The Story of Combs My Village*
Boden, F. W. 'Notes on Woodeaves Mill', *DM*, 3 no 6 (Oct 1965)
Chapman, D. *The Early Factory Masters* (Newton Abbot, 1967)
Daniel, Clarence. 'Industries of Eyam', *DM*, 4 pt 1 (March 1967)
Evans, Seth. *Bradwell Ancient and Modern* (1912)
Haddington, Peter. 'Ghost Valley of the River Goyt', *DC* (Feb–March 1958)
Jackson, J. Wilfrid. 'Cressbrook and Litton Mills', *DM*, 3 no 6 (Oct 1965)
Mackenzie, M. H. 'The Bakewell Cotton Mill and the Arkwrights', *DAJ*, 79 (1959)
Mackenzie, M. H. 'Calver Mill and its Owners', *DAJ*, 83 (1963)
Mackenzie, M. H. 'Cressbrook and Litton Mills 1779–1835, Part 1', *DAJ*, 88 (1968)
Massey, John H. 'The Silk Mills of Macclesfield' (April 1959), Thesis in Central Library, Macclesfield
Parker, Vanessa. 'The Calver Mill Buildings', *DAJ*, 83 (1963)
Rainow Women's Institute. *A Village History* (1952)
Rathbone, Clifford. Articles in *Macclesfield Courier* (Jan–Feb 1956) and *Macclesfield Express* (1958)
Roberts, James. *History of Wetton* (1900)
Shawcross, W. H. *Some Notices of Castleton and its Old Inhabitants AD 1645 to AD 1837* (1903)
Smith, William. 'With Camera and Pen', *Macclesfield Times* (1935)
Thornhill, Robert. 'The Arkwright Cotton Mill at Bakewell', *DAJ*, 79 (1959)
Youlgreave Women's Institute. *Youlgreave and its Neighbourhood* (1931)

CHAPTER FIVE (*Water*. Page 124)

Barber, William. *Brief History and Guide of the Village of Tintwistle* (2nd ed, 1969)
Derwent Valley Water Board. *A short history of the undertaking*
Holmfirth Express (publisher). *Complete Account of the Holmfirth Flood* (1910)
Parkin Bros, Huddersfield (publisher). *Account of the Holmfirth Flood* (1885)
Sheffield City Council Water Committee. *The Water Supply of Sheffield and District*
Terrey, William. *History and Description of the Sheffield Waterworks* (1924)

CHAPTER SIX (*Agriculture*. Page 137)

Carr, J. P. 'Open Field Agriculture in Mid-Derbyshire', *DAJ*, 83 (1963)
Fussell, G. E. 'Four Centuries of Farming Systems in Derbyshire 1500–1900', *DAJ* (1951)
Glover, Stephen. *The Peak Guide* (1830)
Hoskins, W. G. *The Making of the English Landscape* (8th ed, 1969)
Jackson, James C. 'Open Field Cultivation in Derbyshire', *DAJ*, 82 (1962)
Jackson, J. Wilfrid. 'Terraced Cultivation at Priestcliffe near Taddington', *DAJ*, 82 (1962)
Raistrick, Arthur. *Pennine Walls* (Clapham, 2nd ed, 1969)
Tate, W. E. 'Enclosure Acts and Awards relating to Derbyshire', *DAJ* (1944–5)
Thomas, F. ' "Celtic Fields" at Blackwell, Taddington', *DAJ*, 81 (1961)

Thomas, F. 'Ancient Field Boundaries at Blackwell, near Taddington', *DAJ*, 83 (1963)

Wightman, W. E. 'Open Field Agriculture in the Peak District', *DAJ*, 81 (1961)

University of Keele. 'A Study of Agricultural Change in the Staffordshire Moorland 1780–1850', *North Staffordshire Journal of Field Studies*, 1 (1961)

CHAPTER SEVEN (*Communications*. Page 157)

Cockerton, R. W. P. 'The Port Way', *DC*, 2 (Jan 1932) and various subsequent issues

Coleman, Terry. *The Railway Navvies* (1965)

Critchlow, Joyce. 'Kingsterndale', *DC* (Oct–Nov 1964)

Hays Wharf Cartage Company. *Transport Saga 1646–1947*

'Manifold'. *The Leek & Manifold Valley Light Railway* (New ed, 1965)

Margery, Ivan D. *Roman Roads in Britain* (3rd ed, 1967)

Moorhouse, Sydney. 'The Peakland Packhorse Way', *DC*, 10 (Jan 1940)

Radley, Jeffrey. 'Peak District Roads prior to the Turnpike Era', *DAJ*, 83 (1963)

Also information kindly supplied by Mr C. R. Clinker.

Acknowledgements

IN writing this book I have been indebted to a considerable number of people who have shown me much kindness and given me valued help in various ways.

I am very grateful to the many parish council members and others in the parishes of the area who have provided me with local information, shown me various sites and talked about their memories of the past. So many have helped in this way that it is impossible to name all of them here, though each is remembered personally by me, with much gratitude. I must, however, specially thank the following who have generously provided me with information from their own research investigations or who have allowed me access to written material in their possession: Mr C. R. Allcock; Mr W. Barber; Mr F. G. Battye; Mr W. H. Bennett; the late Mr T. J. Brindley; Mr Clarence Daniel; Mr Cyril Evans; Mr S. Garside; Mr R. Orton; The Honourable Dorothy Pickford; Mr Robert Thornhill and Miss J. Wadsworth.

My thanks are due to owners and occupiers who have allowed me to inspect sites on their land or premises; and to commercial firms and public undertakings, including the respective water authorities concerned within the national park, for relevant and historical details which they have kindly supplied. I have much appreciated the co-operation and assistance of the librarians and archivists in the various centres and also that of the Director and members of the staff of the Peak Park Planning Board.

For reading separate parts of the manuscript, and for their criticism, authoritative advice and encouragement, I sincerely thank: Dr J. Wilfrid Jackson; Miss Nellie Kirkham; Mr L. Willies; Mr P. F. Dagger; the late Mr Jeffrey Radley; Miss M. H. Mackenzie; Mr L. M. Waud; Mr R. W. P. Cockerton and Mr C. R. Clinker.

To those who have kindly provided me with material for illustrations (whose names are given in the preliminary pages) also go my thanks, as well as to my publishers and their staff for their helpful efficiency throughout the book's production.

My husband, as always, has been to me a constant source of encouragement and co-operation and I thank him and our son and daughter for their interest and for their happy acceptance of the minor domestic inconveniences which the work has caused.

Index

References to illustrations are printed in italics